Nurse Jamie's Botox Diaries:

Real Stories From a Fake World

Nurse Jamie's
Botox Diaries:
Real Stories From a Fake World

JAMIE SHERRILL

Edited by Stuart K. Robinson

The Red Carpet Press

The Red Carpet Press
287 S. Robertson Blvd.
Suite 477
Beverly Hills, CA 90211

Printed in the United States of America

First Printing, September, 2007
10 9 8 7 6 5 4 3 2 1

ISBN 978-0-9797286-0-0

Photo credits:
Front cover photograph by Dan Warner
Back cover photograph by Robert Raphael

Cover design by Peter Limber
Interior book design by JustYourType.biz

Contact Nurse Jamie at:

Nurse Jamie C/O
The Red Carpet Press
287 S. Robertson Blvd. Suite 477
Beverly Hills, CA 90211

www.nursejamie.com

ACKNOWLEDGEMENTS

First and foremost, to my loving husband, Dan Warner– a gifted actor, photographer and friend who never complained, only supported me when I was engrossed in finishing this project.

To my Mom and Dad – I want to thank them for giving me the intelligence, personality, ability to work my ass off, and the education to make this book happen.

To the men and women who have been my patients and friends – You inspired me to write this book. I hope it will help you keep your sense of humor when engaging in Beauty Warfare.

Thank you to Belle Visage, especially Tina Keshishian and Inez Dunst, for providing me with such a beautiful work environment and all the super-expensive, hottest and latest equipment for me to play with.

To my sisters Patti and Peggy, who laughed and listened to my endless ramblings.

To my dear friends Cassondra, Scot, and Kate for all of their team spirit. I cannot thank you enough.

I wish to express my deep appreciation to my amazing editor, and my mentor, Stuart K. Robinson, who basically challenged me to put "these stories in a book."

To my Mamaw Joyce for always wanting me look my best before she would take me to town

CONTENTS

Foreword by Inez Dunst	ix
Introduction	xi
It Started with Teddy	1
Miss Drop-Dead-Gorgeous Oscar Nominee and Socialite	9
Scary Cosmetic Halloween	15
The Aging-But-Still-Spunky Comic Genius Diva	25
Botox: Fact and Fiction	31
The Poster Girl	37
The Iceman Cometh	45
The Moth and the Flame	53
Genesis	65
Undercover with Hollywood Royalty	73
Errors and Omissions	79
Errors and Omissions 2	93
Biography	103
Mr. Handsome-But-Aging Soap Opera Star	111
An Un-Hollywood Story	115
All in a Day's Work	125
Rock Star Pulls a Boner	131
The PCOS Kid	137
Mr. Yummy, Mr. White-Hot, Mr. Eye Candy	145
French Swamp Lady	155
The Hiv	161
Teddy is Forgiven	169

FOREWORD

Living in Los Angeles, the avalanche of options for self-improvement can often become overwhelming, holding the meek back from truly life-altering enhancements that often take less effort than finding the perfect pair of jeans. As a business owner and mother of a celebrity, I have encountered countless experts who claim to provide miraculous quick-fixes, but often their hype only detracts from the real deal; or worse, they under- or oversell what really exists, pushing unsuspecting people into the realm of frozen faces and trout-mouths, and keeping others from seeking out the benefits of the cosmetic treatments available today.

Jamie Sherrill has been in the world of beauty for almost her entire life, and she views it through the eyes of someone who has tested every treatment on herself and reaped not only the beauty benefits but the improved confidence as well. Every day, she helps her patients toss aside the stigmas that surround medical beauty treatments and empowers them to address their aesthetic challenges. But don't be fooled – she is no used-car salesman of Botox! She's just as likely to say no to unneeded treatments and turn the addicted away to seek help.

Jamie is the person I send my family and friends to, and now with this book, no matter where you live or how much money you have, you have direct access to the mind of one of the foremost industry experts and elite medical spa nurses. Rich and famous women and men from all over the world come to my spa to seek Jamie's advice, and now the inspiring stories she's seen, as well as insight into every tip, treatment and product, are condensed into this all-access book, no plane reservations required.

So sit back, relax, and enjoy.

Inez Dunst
Co-Owner of Belle Visage
and Mother of Kirsten Dunst

INTRODUCTION

It's three a.m. Most of the sane people on the planet are fast asleep. Not me. My telephone is ringing off the hook. This is not an unusual occurrence. In fact, it is perhaps one of the tamest aspects of this rollercoaster ride that has become my life. I use the term 'rollercoaster" in the truest sense I know: wild, unpredictable, enough to make me scream, and as I hang on for dear life with my knuckles the color of Michael Jackson's forehead, I am loving every second of it. This is the life I have chosen, and I wouldn't change it for the world.

The phone rings its fourth ring before clicking on the machine. I am screening, of course. But I know who is calling even before I hear the voice.

It's Marilyn Monroe.

Relax.

It's not really Marilyn Monroe, though it is a star of her same stature – but I'm not going to use her name. This book is not the *Enquirer*, the *Star*, or any other tell-all tabloid. Don't get me wrong. I *will* tell all. I just don't choose to mention the real names of the people who have become my clients. At least not while they're alive. So, unfortunately for her, Marilyn will do just fine. The secrets of the living, you'll have to squeeze out of somebody else. On the other hand, when I say Marilyn Monroe, you can pretty easily narrow down the list of modern-day stars. That's your prerogative.

Why, you may wonder, is Marilyn dialing my number at this ungodly hour? Am I her drug dealer? Her bookie? Her own personal Heidi Fleiss? Or could I be her manager, agent, or shrink? The truth is, none of those people could be as important to Marilyn at this hour as I am.

I am her cosmetic nurse.

Yes, it's true. A nurse, better equipped than her esthetician, and ready, willing, and able to go into far more detail than her doctor ever would.

Yes, I'm the person who keeps the world's most beautiful people looking beautiful long after Mother Nature has announced other plans for them. The ravages of time, the elements, an unhealthy diet and lifestyle, and even acts of God are no match for my restorative skills. If indeed the old song is correct in saying "Beauty's only skin deep," I have made it my mission to ensure that this sacred territory remains unblemished for all of those with the desire and the cash to maintain the perfection that God surely intended.

I pick up the phone, of course. Marilyn's need is real and, for her, painful.

She has a magazine cover shoot later in this day, after the sun will have actually risen, though perhaps more willingly than I will. This photo session will be painful enough without the added agony of a small army of dark hairs on Marilyn's upper lip. Understand, the average woman might be able to get away with the presence of these hairs (though my philosophy is she's a fool to allow it), but Marilyn, who is under a microscopic scrutiny from every person she encounters, even when popping into the local grocery store for an emergency jar of peanut butter, does not have the luxury of such nonchalance. Every woman in America, it seems, is waiting for the chance to tell anyone who will listen that she spotted Marilyn at Smart & Final and "Girl, she's not near as pretty as they make her look on the big screen." Who of us can stand that kind of pressure? Certainly not Nurse Jamie! And what's good enough for Nurse Jamie is good enough for Marilyn.

Like you, I often wonder why the stars who come to me for treatments can't take care of their business during normal hours like everybody else. But I have never been a star, so I guess I have no idea what the pressures are in the lifestyle of the Marilyns of the world whose livelihood depends so heavily on the preservation of their beauty.

So, rather than judge, I just do my best to provide the services that keep these people on the pedestal the American public demands they remain perched upon.

Plus, my clientele is not nearly all stars. Not all women either. Men and women of all sizes, shapes, backgrounds, and walks of life come to me with only one thing in common: they want to look their best. And I do everything in my power to make sure that their wish comes true.

If only it didn't have to happen at three in the morning!

These are my stories: some of them outrageous, some of them ridiculous, some touching, and all of them true. Maybe I've written them for you to share so I can keep a tenuous grip on what's *real*. When you spend the better part of each day dealing with *fake* noses, breasts, eyebrows, and often personalities, it feels kinda good to tell it like it is. I would also like to say that, for all the bad rap they get, many of my clients have proven to be some of the warmest, truest people I have ever met. So, the saying really is true that you can't judge a book by its cover.

Okay, so I happen to have the power to make that antique cover look like a first edition! And yes, sometimes – okay, *most* times – the road to Botox City is paved with eccentricity and downright insanity. But, I wouldn't have it any other way.

I pray that my clients will have one-tenth the sense of humor in reading these stories that it took me to endure living through them. And those of them, and of you, who raise an eyebrow at any of what is written here… well, at least there will be no wrinkles in your forehead when that eyebrow goes up.

Enjoy!

 It Started with Teddy

Blame it on Teddy Wickman. He started it all.

Teddy Wickman was my first love, at the ripe age of nine. I thought he was just the most beautiful thing on the planet, and I prayed each night that he would feel the same about me. I would watch him across the playground at school, marveling at what a perfect-looking human being he was. I was up at the crack of dawn each day making sure I looked my best, waiting for the day Teddy would take notice of me and we could begin a fairy-tale relationship for the ages. Yes, I admit I was dramatic even back then. But if you had met Teddy Wickman, marvelous Teddy Wickman, my Teddy Wickman, you would understand.

Actually, Teddy was an average-looking kid with prepubescent acne, a slight overbite and a Dennis the Menace cowlick. But to nine-year-old Jamie he was Adonis himself, and I couldn't wait for the day we would actually talk face to face; the day he would share his feelings for me, which just had to be immense if there was any justice in the universe.

As always, the big day came sooner than expected. Of all places it happened in the lunch line at school, where an altercation between the Soup Nazi and Michael Biederman caused a sizeable delay in the ant farm-like line of sliding trays. In this lull I found myself right next to my dream, my Teddy. It all happened so fast I could hardly process it. Just as I had pictured it so many times, he looked over at me and smiled. Then as I also envisioned, he looked me up and down and opened his mouth to speak:

"Oh my God, you have hairy arms!"

Though I am alive today, I must insist… that killed me.

Thus began the "long-sleeved shirt era" for young Jamie Sherrill. Summer, winter… who cares? Long-sleeved shirts at all times. If they had made a long-sleeved swimsuit I would have had one. I would sooner show you the crack of my butt than have you see the woolly arms that killed my love affair with Teddy Wickman.

It didn't take me long to notice other major imperfections in my appearance. At nine years old, I already had a good start on a pretty impressive "Fu Manchu," and let me tell you I was not happy about it. I knew, even then, that something had to be done about these things that made me insecure about my looks. I secretly made a promise that one day I'd fix all of the things that bothered me about my appearance. I would not lose the next Teddy Wickman simply because I could not convince my own body to stop growing hair in places I did not authorize.

This had to be the start of my obsession with the human body, and my fascination with any and all techniques that might make a person's appearance easier on the eye. My mantra became, "Why should anyone walk around unhappy with their appearance if there is a way to make it better?" Or at least make it *look* better.

And now, here I am, trained, licensed and committed to making the world a more beautiful place – one face at a time.

These are my stories. This is my truth.

If any part of it seems ugly to you... well, we can always give it a little touchup.

Don't get me wrong. I love what I do. It's the path I chose, and I chose it for a reason. I really am committed to the idea of helping every person look his or her best at all times. Believe me, I have experienced the difference one little fix can make in a person's life. Not having to worry about everyone staring at your arms or your neck changes the way you participate in events and in life. We get so short a time in this life as it is... why not enjoy it to the fullest instead of hanging back in the corner because you're afraid your hairy upper lip will catch the light? I know, a lot of people say you should just get better at accepting your flaws and "loving yourself for who you are." Give me a break! If I can spend a few painless laser sessions getting rid of a mustache Nature should never have given me in the first place, I can spend my time loving myself and other people without wasting any love on my upper lip. Think about it. One session and you never have to shave, pluck, wax, cover with makeup, or ever even think about that unwanted hair again. Now I can focus on accepting some real flaws, like my tendency to slip and fall flat on my ass in upscale social settings.

While I'm scrambling on the floor to retrieve my purse and the pearls that broke and rolled all over the room, I'm chanting, "I love myself, I love myself, I love my *self*!" and have no time to wonder whether I shaved my armpits well enough.

And please, don't try to tell me that people don't notice those things. Tell me you've never had a conversation with an otherwise attractive woman who has a mole adjacent to her lower lip with one large hair growing smack in the middle of it. No matter how liberal and humane a person you are, can you help but obsess on that hair, watching it bob up and down, back and forth with each word that comes out of her mouth? Meanwhile, you're in absolute terror that at any moment you're going to completely blow it, saying the one thing you least want to say, like: "These egg rolls are delicious! Do you want some *mole*?" Or: "If you want more egg rolls you'd better *hairy*." Who needs all of that? Just get the damned hair removed and the stupid mole lasered! Stop making me work so hard just to chat with you at a party! I said it, I meant it, and I represent it.

Besides, cosmetic work is just like anything else – it takes some time to catch on. I believe in my heart that Botox will soon become the new hair highlights. Remember that? How it used to be such an ugly secret if you had color added to your hair? You had to creep around in back alleys to get it done, like you were sneaking off to an abortionist. Then, when people commented on your hair, you had to make up some wild-assed story about a last-minute weekend trip to Aruba, where you "got all kinds of sun" that brought out the highlights in your hair – even though it didn't give your pasty white butt one bit of color. All of this to cover up the fact that you want a few lousy streaks of blonde in your hair. A bright red wig people could accept. But adding a few highlights was considered more shameful than French-kissing your brother (thank God I never had a brother!). But now we live in an enlightened age in which hair coloring is not only acceptable, you can practically have it done during a job interview and no one even bats an eyelid. I can have lunch with you on Tuesday wearing a cute little pixie-cut pageboy, and then run into you at the post office Wednesday morning with hair down to my knees, and no one will seem to even notice. But the mention of the word Botox clears a crowded room as though you yelled "Fire!" in a packed theater.

Just wait. Pretty soon, when people realize how simple it is to erase five or ten years' worth of crow's feet and wrinkles in a single session, people will be flocking to get it. Botox centers will be the frozen yogurt palaces of the future. Starbucks will offer free Internet access and a Botox and skin peel while you wait for your twenty-dollar latté. Think about it. How many older married men will be running off to find a college co-ed to dump their wives for when the wife has the skin of a twenty-two-year-old? Not to mention the boobs, flat tummy, hairless chin' plus the brains and savvy of a woman who's been around the block? College girls won't be able to find a date!

But that day, for now, is in the future. For the present, I have to deal with the eccentricities of a clientele who can't live without my services, but would sooner be horsewhipped in public than admit that they ever had the tiniest bit of work done. And, for better or for worse, most of those beloved clients are a part of the entertainment industry. Show business. Hollyweird.

I say "for better or for worse" because working with the population of Tinseltown has its plusses and minuses. On the upside, celebrities are the best clients in the world for people like me whose business has high liability when things go wrong. There isn't much margin for error when you're injecting a weakened form of botulism a quarter of an inch from a patient's eyeball. But celebrities won't take you to court when a rare mishap occurs. Heck, they don't even want their *families* to know they had work done, much less the legal system, the press, and eventually the whole world. They will never take you public. Instead they make up a quick story about a last-minute trip to Aruba....

But, on the downside, these customers can be, to say the least, a little high-strung, and often paralyzingly neurotic.

Miss Drop-Dead Gorgeous
Oscar Nominee and Socialite

I should have known when the call came in that this one was going to be a headache and a nightmare. I really should listen to my instincts more. I'm almost always right. But it's hard to say no when a top celeb like MISS DROP-DEAD-GORGEOUS OSCAR NOMINEE AND SOCIALITE calls nearly in tears because the Golden Globe Awards are this weekend, she's a presenter, and she HAS TO HAVE A TOUCHUP around the eyes!

Now, let me interject here that this woman needs a touchup like I need a third breast. I mean, we are talking about a perfect-looking face and body. Look up 'flawless' in the dictionary and I can tell you whose face will be positioned right next to the definition. But who am I to tell this goddess that she can't have a little Botox® if it makes her feel more comfortable on a world stage as a billion viewers try to find a reason that they are as attractive as she is?

So, reluctantly I make an appointment for the wee hours of the night – a time when, I guess, no press or paparazzi would ever be following the actions of their favorite prey. Miss DDGONAS is so grateful, and so accommodating when she arrives you'd think I had donated her one of my kidneys. But now that she's here I feel like

I have to remind her that the big event is only two days away, and one of the setbacks of Botox is that it can occasionally cause a small temporary bruise while it does its magic. I hesitate to mention it, but with the Golden Globes coming up so soon, I want to cover all the bases.

At the mere mention of the possibility that the treatment might not happen, one of her perfectly shaped lips begins to tremble. I'm starting to think I may have a situation on my hands here. She begins to plead with me to go ahead with the treatment. Hey, I'm not trying to run a power game here. If she wants it, she should be able to have it. After all, she's the big star, and I'm just an idiot who should be curled up in my cozy bed instead of sneaking every man's fantasy on two legs into my office at this ungodly hour. I tell her that I will do it... but there's a tiny chance it will bruise.

I ask her if she has taken any blood thinners of any variety in the last few days.

"None. Just do it."

I hesitate. "Any alcohol or St. John's Wort?"

"No."

"Not even wine?" I continue.

"Can we just get on with this?"

Now it is clear she won't be needing my kidney. In fact I can take it and shove it.

So, with these alarm bells going off in my head, I make her sign a paper stating that all of the above-mentioned statements are true. We do the session.

On the way out the door, Miss DDGONAS does recall that maybe she did have some wine earlier in the day – but her euphoria has now turned to optimism, and she is, for a moment, undaunted when I mention that a pencil eraser-sized bruise just might be in her future. But suddenly as my words sink in, she begins to hyperventilate, and starts getting faint at the mere mention of the word. I have to help her to a seat and stabilize her breathing, while I reassure her, "It's not permanent." She is, needless to say, NOT reassured, but leaves on wobbly legs anyway.

At six a.m. I receive the worried call.

At six-twenty a.m. I receive the panicked call.

Then the angry call. And the hysterical call. The whimpering call. The threatening call and the lost little girl call.

"What can we do? You've got to fix this. I'll be ruined. You have ruined my career. I may have to leave the country!"

Can I remind you that we're talking about a faint, pin-sized discoloration beneath the skin?

I suggest Arnica and ice, but Miss DDGONAS is past the point of reason, and seems to only derive pleasure from dialing and redialing my cell phone number. And let me assure you that on the thirtieth call my response was no different from the first. And I must honestly say I felt her pain. I know what it's like to feel like every eye in the room is fixed on that single blemish in the middle of your face, your being, your soul! But really, what can I do?

I do what any red-blooded American girl would do in times of war: I call my mom. Mom, who utters two syllables, which seem like they should be engraved on stone tablets and carried down the mountain:

"Makeup."

The Golden Globes went off without a hitch. The night was a big success, and MISS DROP-DEAD-GORGEOUS OSCAR NOMINEE AND SOCIALITE was able to avoid leaving the country.

Of course a few days later she did once again dial my cell phone, this time to tell me that she's been worried sick about another issue. She hasn't slept for days thinking about this, and must insist that I write up the late night visit as a laser treatment, in case some enterprising front desk employee might find the paperwork with the dreaded "B" word on it and sell a copy of the work order to the highest bidding tabloid with the headline: ACTRESS KEEPS GLOBES GOLDEN WITH BOTOX!

I, of course, once again feel her pain. What do I care how it's written up? In signing off, she swears to me that she will never do Botox again, after all of the stress she endured after this experience. Though I again feel her pain, I can't help but remark:

"Girlfriend, talk to me in a few years."

I humbly, gratefully, gleefully hang up.

But this is not nearly the end of the downside.

 Scary Cosmetic Halloween

Believe me, I understand why so many people are down on cosmetic surgery. I get it that there are lots of aspects of my profession that are easy to hate if you don't really understand them or know the whole story. And some parts are hate-able even if you *do* know the whole story. Heck, show me a business where that *isn't* true. I was a flight attendant for five years, and if the average person knew some of the things I know about the airline industry, they'd never get on a plane ever again. Ask anyone who's worked in a restaurant what would happen if you let the customers enter through the kitchen.

Plus, some of the things you read about cosmetic surgery are enough to curl your hair. We've all heard that Botox treatments are nothing more than botulism, one of the deadliest substances on earth, being injected into your skin. And one look at that freak they call "Catwoman" on the tabloid shows because she's so addicted to corrective treatments that she looks like a tabby cat, and you probably can assume that underneath my blonde hair are two pointy horns and three sixes etched into my scalp. But you've also read that Britney Spears gave birth to an alien baby! So, don't hate the playa, hate the game!

It's true – in any profession there are always a few bad apples who make it hard for the rest. I have always tried to be a good apple – a delicious apple, if you will. I don't believe in *too* much of anything – especially cosmetic enhancement. I think my work is in one strange way like a movie director's – if you are seeing the director's work, you're probably not appreciating the movie. I don't want my clients looking like they just saw a ghost, or like they can't wipe the demonic grimace of a smile off their waxy faces. Just as their appearance shouldn't be marred by wrinkles and lines, age spots and warts, or unsightly inappropriate hairs, it should also not be ruined by "the Joan Rivers effect." If you see one of my clients looking like they just had a tray of ice cubes shoved up their butt, please shoot me. But that's not going to happen, because I take pride in the work I do – treating each person's face and body like a delicate canvas, and like a sacred temple. Isn't it great to know that your armpits and the inside of your nose are hairless holy shrines!

Seriously, I can't handle people walking around looking like Frankenstein's monster, and I won't do that kind of work. I know there are many who will, but not this girl. In fact, I have to tell you about one of my most frightening evenings ever…

It was the week before Halloween, and I was meeting a nurse friend of mine at La Scala for dinner. She had been invited by patients that she had befriended while working for one of the doctors on a short-lived-but-stupid-and-popular-reality-show, which involved cosmetic enhancement. Because my friend and I work in the same industry, she thought I would be interested in meeting some of this doctor's clients. Plus, she informed me, they all have really interesting stories to tell. How could I resist?

Let me preface this story by telling a totally separate tale to give you a sense of the frame of mind I was in coming into this evening:

Not long before this La Scala dinner night, one of my friends set me up to be "punked" on a show that Jamie Kennedy used to do long before *Punked* became a hit. My friend, of course, was 'the accomplice" and I was to be "the pigeon." Under some false pretense that I don't even remember, we were supposed to meet for dinner at a cool little sushi place not far from where I live. The idea was that Jamie Kennedy was going to dress up in a wig and brown contacts, passing himself off as a kind of kamikaze sushi chef, and somehow was gonna make me do all kinds of embarrassing stuff. You know, I was supposed to get flustered and crazy and say all kinds of hilarious yet humiliating stuff just before Jamie whips off his disguise to show all of America what a nitwit I really am.

Well, I don't know why, but as soon I walked into the restaurant I said to my friend, "Look at that guy dressed up like a Japanese sushi chef – he must be an actor!" Of course my friend immediately tried to tell me I was crazy, and that the guy "is a regular chef here." Well that might work on most people, but not on someone who notices tiny flaws in people for a living. I told my friend, "You must be high! He is an actor… Look, it's so obvious!" Once again she denied it and made a huge effort to change the subject.

Hey, fine with me. If some actor wants to parade around trying to look like a Japanese sushi chef, what business is that of mine? So we sat down and proceeded to get ready to place our orders.

Well, it didn't take long for Jamie Kennedy to come over to our table prepared to start up some shtick. But before he could speak I elbowed my friend and said, "Look… see the makeup on him? And those are totally brown contacts in his eyes." I actually point my finger in his face. Now keep in mind, I'm not saying I'm like Sherlock Holmes or anything. I totally hadn't figured out that this whole thing had anything to do with me. I just thought it was hilarious that this guy, whoever he was, was trying to pass himself off as Japanese. I actually started thinking maybe he was pulling one over on the management of the restaurant, because if they found out he was a white kid from the Palisades or someplace they'd never give him a job in an authentic sushi restaurant. I felt kinda bad about outing the guy, but my friend kept insisting so vehemently that I was wrong, I just couldn't let it drop.

Well, pretty soon Jamie Kennedy's production assistant came out of hiding and ended our hidden camera scenes because I wasn't playing along, and in fact ruined the episode and spoiled all the fun. They were actually kind of pissed at me – like it was my fault their little prank fell apart. I couldn't help thinking, "maybe if you'd hire a decent makeup artist so the greasepaint isn't smearing down the guy's chin, people would fall for your transparent gags." Needless to say, everyone involved was disappointed, and they kicked us out of the restaurant so they could try to emotionally scar some other sucker for life.

So that's the first story.

Now fast-forward a couple of months to La Scala. We walk into this posh restaurant and are immediately escorted to a table for eight, where we were to join six people who were all clients of Dr. Leather-Skinned Reality Show Quack. Megan is, as fits the story, working for and sleeping with said doctor. I sat down at the head of the table without really looking closely at my dinner mates because I was fending off a captain and an army of waiters each more eager than the next to relieve me of my coat, which I had no intention of removing. Earlier while driving to the restaurant I had wondered why all of these people whose only common bond was the "work" they'd had done would gather for dinners together. Megan had informed me that one of her clients was a very wealthy man from the South. This guy Mr. Moneybags and his boyfriend regularly fly their closest friends in from Louisiana to get Botox treatments and cosmetic work from Dr. Leather.

Finally, as introductions begin, I take my first good look at the other guests at the table, and my first thought is that everyone is wearing a mask. I can't help glancing quickly around to see if I can spot Jamie Kennedy ready to leap from a nearby hiding place, exacting his own very special brand of revenge for my earlier destruction of his mind-numbingly brilliant prank show.

Every person at the table has a face so distorted they remind me of those movie posters you see in video stores for that old classic horror film *The Abominable Dr. Phibes*. Now sure, we've all seen it: the overdone facelift, the forehead and eyebrows pulled so high the person has a permanent expression of unadulterated astonishment. Heck, even my friend Megan has gone "trout mouth," so I'm almost used to seeing it – but not six of them at the same table all at once. This is like a visit to the Hollywood Wax Museum – except the sculptures are talking, slurping martinis and chewing breadsticks! Now my imagination begins to get the better of me. I suddenly convince myself that this is going to be a hidden camera show where a host will ask me how to correct these overdone, over-pulled faces. I prepare myself for the same P.A. from the sushi place to run over shouting, "We got you this time, you stupid bitch!"

Two of the friends are twin sisters in their 60's with faces pulled tighter than a pair of dolphin shorts at the Halloween Parade in West Hollywood. They apparently still work as flight attendants for a major airline. I cringe at the thought of finding myself somewhere over the Pacific Ocean at twenty thousand feet, just dozing off, only to awaken to these two mugs leering down at me asking if I want to purchase a snack box.

I am seated next to a woman whose forehead lift scar is still fresh, daring me not to stare at it or to barf my breadsticks onto the starched linen tablecloth. Madame Scarface is wearing a blonde, Dolly Parton old-school-style wig and about seven-and-a-half pounds of eye shadow and lipstick. I make conversation, shouting over *The Twilight Zone* theme which is blasting in my head. Somehow we get on the subject of her many ex-husbands/ boyfriends – one of which, I'm told, used to play James Bond. This female Tony Montana hints at some very mysterious stuff, which Megan later interprets as a tale of the woman's playwright late husband who was found dead in the trunk of his car with his hands cut off after receiving numerous threats from the Panamanian government to stop writing his current script about corruption in Panama.

As if these people's faces are not scary enough, this tale starts getting to me, making me wonder if I could continue giving Botox treatments with two artificial hands *à la* Captain Hook. The insanity can only be topped by a statement from Mr. Moneybags telling me, "If you see me in public, you don't know me and you don't know why I am here. Get it?" I reply, "Oh yes, of course!"

I am used to that – laugh, laugh – and I was gone. Driving home I keep checking my rearview mirror to see if I'm being followed. Yeah really, I'm that freaked out. Who could be following me? I don't know – the Panamanian government? Jamie Kennedy? The entire cast of *Night of the Living Dead*? Remind me never to have a facelift done by Dr. Leather.

Later, when my sanity begins to return, I regain my sense of humor and start thinking maybe that would be a cool costume for next Halloween: Ms. Excessive Facelift in a Dolly Parton wig. All I have to do is put a large tight rubber band around the top of my forehead, maintain that shocked expression like my wallet was just pinched, add a ton of gaudy makeup, a dress that's just a little too tight, and go around insanely grinning at everyone even when nothing is funny. Perfect!

But I can only think that these people *like* the way they look. Think about it. They could not possibly have all had the surgery at the same time. So one would have to have had the treatment first, gone back to Tennessee or wherever they live, and the others saw them and said, "Wow, you look pretty good!" Then the original zombie probably said, "I sheell fretty good, shank you!" That's how tight the face must have been right after the treatment. And then the others thought to themselves, "Hmmm, I think I would like to do that to my face as well." Next thing you know, each of them was booked on Mr. Moneybag Airlines headed for Dr Frankenstein's laboratory.

Whew! Just thinking about it makes me want to check my trunk for dead bodies.

So, I guess sometimes you can't hate the game – hate the playa!

 The Aging-But-Still-Spunky
Comic Genius Diva

I treat three celebrities who are all from the cast of a classic sitcom – they are all my clients. Cool-and-Actually-Surprisingly-Down-To-Earth client number one mentioned to me that an Aged-Former-Oscar-Nominee-and-Comedic-Genius was up for a Golden Globe and wanted to know if I could do anything about her facial pigmentation. CAASDTE phoned me first to feel out the idea, about two months before the Golden Globes, and I said that I would love to see this new client – I found her movies very funny. I told CAASDTE to just have her call and make an appointment. Well, I did not hear anything from Miss Aged Former, which is normal. Sometimes people lose their nerve or think better of having work done, or their schedule gets so busy they can't take any downtime to allow the procedure to heal. No big deal.

Then one week before the awards ceremony my cell phone rings. Miss Aged Former is calling, asking – no, more like *instructing* me to come to her house to look at her skin. I request that she come to me in case I need to use the pigment laser, which is too large to transport. That idea was out of the question, and Miss Aged Former was actually upset that I suggested it. As if no one on the planet had ever done anything but obey her every command. I mean, her movies weren't *that* funny, for cryin' out loud. So to calm her down and maybe avoid a long drive to her house, I suggest that maybe her pigment isn't that bad, and perhaps there would be a product that could help. Out of the question again. I must come to her house immediately. Okay.

The patient lives in West Los Angeles – not really my neck of the woods – and besides, I know a whole lot of stuff, but there are some areas where I make all of the blonde jokes in the world come true. "Directions" is one of those areas. So, needless to say, I was having trouble finding the place. So I call Miss Aged Former, who proceeds to yell at me for not having a GPS in my car. I guess in her world everyone has a GPS. But in my world – the one I think most people live in – a GPS is a luxury, not a staple. I apologize for my lack and request the directions, which I must add she had some trouble giving – and she lives there!

Upon arrival at her really fabulous condo, I ring and ring but no one answers, and I begin to wonder if I've actually found the right place after all. But after minutes of ringing, finally the door is opened by a scruffy-looking ten-year-old boy who stares blankly at me, never says a word, then walks away – I never see him again. Now I am inside, but have no idea where to go. Suddenly I am greeted by the blast of an intercom, with Miss Aged's voice announcing, "Come back to my bedroom. I am not feeling well and I am in bed." Okay. I have never been in this condo before so I don't know where the bedroom is, and of course my ten-year-old guide has disappeared. I guess I'm supposed to have another GPS in my purse to navigate my way through a stranger's house – but sadly, I don't. I start walking forward, only to pass a room with a baby in a swing all by itself, just swinging back and forth with no adult in sight. Then four dogs come out of nowhere, sniffing and poking me until they are satisfied, and "the voice" returns overhead and impatiently demands, "Where are you?" How the hell do I know where I am – I feel like I am in an episode of *Northern Exposure*—very surreal. But I keep walking, venturing deeper into the inner sanctum.

The next room has a thirty-something, half-naked woman playing a piano by herself, drinking wine. I do not think she even knew I was in the condo – just sitting there playing some eerie tune over and over again. Should I assume that she is "watching" the baby? I doubt it. More likely Tim Burton is directing this entire thing, and the baby is a hologram that will disappear at any moment. Then I hear "the voice" once again, but this time from a nearby room, not just from the intercom. I walk toward the voice, entering a very dark bedroom, where I think my new client is ensconced in a large bed. I say "I think" because I really can't see much of anything in this room, but as she said, she is not feeling well and does not want me to turn on the lights. Well, I am good but I cannot do cosmetic work in the dark – I insist we turn on some lights. After a lengthy negotiation she agrees to one little dim-bulbed light, which I gratefully turn on. Sure enough, there in the bed is Miss-Funny-In-Movies-Not-Funny-In-Life.

It gets worse. Even in the dimly-lit bedroom I can see the patient is covered in pigmented lesions – she is in dire need of a series of IPL (Intense Pulsed Light – a photo facial that repairs broken capillaries, stimulates growth of new collagen cells, and lightens pigmentation).

She also possibly will need a Fraxel® treatment – basically a skin resurfacing laser treatment. Both of those machines are too large to transport, and certainly nothing you would use in a dimly-lit condo bedroom. There is nothing I can do for her tonight but tell her to come and see me at the office where all of my equipment lives. She can actually use her GPS to find me! Of course this is all unacceptable to her, and apparently a secret signal that she should begin screaming. But hey, I win this round simply because I cannot produce an IPL laser machine out of my ass.

I explain that I am booked already this week but as a favor to the client who referred her I will stay late to accommodate Miss Aged. But remember, it's days before the Golden Globes, and I have to explain to her that the spots will look worse before they look better, and it will take about ten days for the scabbing from the treatment to come off.

"TEN DAYS!!!!" she screams at me. "The award show dinner's start is in *three* days, you idiot, you cow!"

Secure in the knowledge that I am not a bovine, I advise her to hire a good makeup artist, as I cannot treat the pigmentation without some small amount of downtime and they will appear darker for the first week. I patiently tell her it would be best to wait until after the awards and to call and make an appointment to have a treatment done, and I dash for the door – past the bouncing baby, past the manic half-naked pianist, with the ten-year-old still nowhere to be seen, and out into the relative sanity of my car.

Of course the next day she calls her friend to complain that I am not willing to help her. My friend doesn't know what to do, and certainly doesn't want to be screamed at by the bedridden powerhouse, so she does what any human being would do: hands the phone to me. I explain again that if she had come in two weeks ago I could have helped her but I would only be making matters worse if we do the treatment tomorrow. She keeps saying she does not understand why I didn't come earlier. I now see that in her world everyone is also a psychic, able to divine the thoughts of people they have never met.

For now, I think I'll stick to my world. Though I might just get myself a GPS.

Botox: Fact and Fiction

.

I'll be the first to admit that I'm afraid of a lot of things. Spiders scare the shit out of me. I'm not a big fan of rollercoasters – too scary. I don't much like watching horror movies right before I go to sleep – keeps me up all night. Giving toasts at weddings has me dripping perspiration, and the very idea of jumping out of an airplane with nothing but a glorified backpack on my back gives me the immediate willies. My husband is at the point where he no longer thinks it's cute. And I don't blame him. I'm a wimp. I can embrace that. Things scare me.

But I am not afraid of Botox. Because I understand Botox. I'm aware that most people don't know enough about Botox to do anything but fear it. So, I want to help you gain that same understanding, so you can let Botox become the friend to you that it has been to me.

Here's the technical lowdown: Botox Cosmetic® is a purified protein produced by the Clostridium botulinum bacterium, which means "nectar of the gods." Yes, let's get it out of the way – Botox is a weakened form of botulism. Now is your cue to start shouting, "Are you crazy? You're gonna inject a highly poisonous bacteria into your own skin?!" Let's not get out of hand here. Think about it. Every vaccination you've ever had in your life is nothing less than that. Trying to avoid tuberculosis? We're gonna inject a weakened dose of – guess what? – good old T.B., straight into your bloodstream. If you've ever traveled abroad, chances are you injected a couple of strains of malaria, typhoid, and diphtheria. Didn't stop you from going to lunch later that day.

So Botox is in that same ballpark, but instead of protecting you from botulism, it reduces the activity of facial muscles that causes you to develop lines over time. The FDA has only approved it for frown lines, but Botox is being administered to all parts of the face to minimize frown lines, crow's feet, and other blemishes that come with aging and stress. As with any cutting-edge technique, I think Botox gets a bad name because some of the practitioners who use it don't use the best judgment in applying it. I mean, you don't have to freeze the patient's entire face, giving them that Donatella Versace look. The old saying is true: "in all things, moderation." That seems obvious to me.

We shouldn't have to be reminding cosmetic specialists that their patients need to come out of the session looking like human beings instead of ancient fossilized artifacts. Is that so much to ask? But when the public sees these laboratory creations, they assume that Botox is a villain, a horrible toxic chemical that will be the ruination of us all. Get a grip on yourself. We're talking about a few crow's feet here.

Really. In one ten-minute treatment – a few tiny injections – the process is activated to create a noticeable improvement in moderate to severe lines over the next few days. The effects last up to four months. Of course, results may vary, and believe me they do. And that's why you go to a professional like me. I know how to monitor your progress, turning the results you get into beauty and well-being.

Everybody thinks that clinics are making a fortune giving Botox treatments. Let me tell you the truth: we offer Botox treatment because it works. And the more people try it, the more they become true believers. And though the cost of the product has even gone up in recent years, the cost to the consumer has dropped. Why? Well, first of all there's more demand for it, so the portions of the expensive mixed product that used to be thrown out after its four-day expiration are now used up immediately. Where it used to take over a week to use up a one-hundred-unit vial (well beyond the four-day expiration), now that supply and more is gone in a day. No waste, no cost. Secondly, as more practitioners discover it, the competition increases, creating the same kind of price wars that gas stations and house movers have. I have been giving Botox treatments for over ten years, and I have not seen a whole lot of unhappy people. In fact, I see quite the contrary. People looking and feeling younger as a result of their newfound confidence.

But don't take my word for it. Follow the example of the three million citizens who have Botox treatments each year. Trust me, there's nothing to be afraid of. And you're getting that from a dyed-in-the-wool scaredy-cat. Heck, at least it's not spiders.

The Poster Girl

Dear Botox,

What can I say but, "I love you?"

Your friend always,

Jamie

I never actually wrote this love note, but I could have. I *do* love Botox. I know it's a weird thing to say, but I do. Now, don't get crazy on me. I'm not really in love with an injectable liquid. I'm in love with what it can do for people. For their self-esteem. For their confidence and comfort level. If you have ever seen, as I have, the difference in the way a person walks after something they have been self-conscious about most of their life has been eliminated, you'll know where my love comes from.

And I'm not just observing this from a distance. I'm proud to say it: I'm the living, breathing, Botox poster girl. In fact, there aren't many treatments I perform on other people that I haven't undergone myself, partly because I feel it's important for me to really be in touch with the procedures I'm performing, and partly because I just love looking younger, fitter and better.

At a very young age I developed a weird moustache (which I refer to as my "two Fu Manchus"). You can imagine how well that goes over when a preteen has a thicker beard than the school custodian. Combine that with the super-hairy arms that my first sweetheart, the aforementioned Teddy Wickman, had the sensitivity to point out, and you can guess that the local kids had a field day with me. Have you any idea how that messes with a person's self-esteem, no matter how otherwise secure they may be?

I also had the thickest "shrub" eyebrows you can imagine. How many times can a young girl have people call her Groucho, saying, "That's the most ridiculous thing I ever heard of," wagging an imaginary cigar, before the girl starts to feel like a creature from another planet? My mom tried her best to comfort me. She'd say, "Those eyebrows are perfect. Do you have any idea how many women on this earth would die to have those full brows? You are the lucky one."

But of course, at age ten or twelve that just isn't enough to erase the laughter on the schoolyard. And certainly not enough to keep me from feeling like the ugliest girl in the state.

So, just imagine the feeling when that same girl grows up to discover that none of those things she's tried to hide her whole life has any control over her. In fact she has the power to wipe them away, never to return. And when that girl learns she has the power and the skill to do the same for others... well, that beats a poke in the eye with a frozen dishrag.

So I've had my share of treatments, and I'm proud of every one.

My personal favorite is laser hair removal. How could it not be? To grow up with a Fu Manchu, constantly trying to keep people from seeing it, is a nightmare.

Add to that the fact that my mom, like most people, warned

me that if I shaved it, it would stimulate hair growth and come back thicker. Now that I'm a registered nurse, I know better. Heck, you don't have to be an R.N. to figure out that if shaving an area stimulated hair growth, every cue-ball-headed businessman with a comb-over would be shaving his way to nirvana until he had locks Fabio would envy. But like any girl would, I listened to my mom's advice. So, to stumble upon laser hair removal and discover that I can actually kill the hair at its root so it never returns was like finding the Holy Grail. I started with my chin, and of course moved to my upper lip. And between that first treatment and today, I have treated every part of my body from below my scalp on down. I challenge you to find a hair on my body anywhere but on top of my head. Of course my husband will have to accompany you on the search.

I am like a baby seal. Hairless and shivering. And I never have to worry about shaving my underarms or my legs. That Sasquatch look my arms once had has been replaced by smooth hairless skin. There are no whiskers on my chin or lip, no nose hairs to pluck, and no embarrassing single curly hairs growing out of my ear like Jack's beanstalk. I have no coat of fur on my tummy or my butt, and best of all, the Groucho Marx eyebrows are a thing of the past, replaced by simple and demure wisps that accent my eyes. Victory! Score: Jamie – one; hair – zero.

I have had Botox treatments in several areas. First I worked on the platysmal bands, that part of the neck that always seems to be the first to show your age or an increase in weight. With proper applications of Botox I was able to make my neck smooth and supple.

I then hit the glabella, that area between the eyebrows that, over time, makes your forehead look like someone wrote the number "eleven" between your eyes. Just a couple of treatments changed the eleven to a zero.

While I was at work in the forehead area, I figured it would be a good idea to do something about those "Shar-Pei" lines, the ones that make you look like you're constantly trying to solve a math equation. Don't get me wrong, I love Shar-Peis. I just don't want one on my head. Next, I smoothed out the outer areas of my eyes. Crow's feet, age lines, whatever you want to call them, I have no use for them. Gone.

I also experimented with a lip plumping procedure (which I really didn't need, but I was curious to see how it looked), that eventually turned out not to be my thing. More on that later.

I was pretty excited when I learned about the advent of mesotherapy (pronounced me-zo, like that watery soup they serve in sushi places with a glob of tofu floating in it), a series of injections that rids parts of the body of excess fat and cellulite, but is more controllable and requires far less downtime than liposuction. I did meso on the backs of my legs to correct an issue brought on by a less inspired decision. More about that later, also.

I had always wanted permanent eyeliner, which sounded like a great idea, and probably would have been had I chosen the right practitioner. But I didn't, so I had laser removal to take the eyeliner away.

Over the years I have had several skin peels, a process in which the outer dying skin is peeled away to reveal a fresh layer beneath. This leaves me with glowing and radiant skin (I'm so glad I get to talk like those soap commercials!).

I also regularly give myself IPL's (Intense Pulse Light). This is also known as a photo facial, a process where a powerful light source fixes broken capillaries and stimulates collagen cells (new skin cells). This procedure is great for reversing the effects of rosacea, and for pigment disorders, but for me it just gives my complexion a tune-up, oil change and lube.

I'm sure if I really thought about it, I'd find other treatments I have done. I have no fear. I'd love to try them all. That way I can, with one hundred percent clear conscience, advise my clients that these services are safe, effective, fast, and the answer to most any cosmetic blemish. After all, all they have to do is look at me – from head to toe. I'm a walking display case of the services I offer. And according to my husband, that ain't bad at all.

The Iceman Cometh

I get new patients in a lot of ways: word of mouth, direct referral from patients or physicians, friends and family. None has ever arrived in a more memorable fashion than "Ice."

Ice was dragged in by his father – literally by the ear. Now, I've heard that saying for years, about being taken somewhere by the ear, and I always thought it was just that: a saying. Until I met Ice and his father. The man was dragging his son into the treatment room with the kid's ear pinched between two fingers. I guess the saying was inspired by the action, because it seemed to be a pretty effective way of getting another person to go wherever you choose to lead them – even if it was against the person's will.

My first instinct was to feel sorry for the kid. I mean, this father was a pretty large guy. It looked like his grip was above average strength, which couldn't bode too well for how the kid's ear must be feeling. Plus, from the look on the dad's face, I couldn't help but speculate that this guy would not make the list of the top million people I'd want to be raised by. And the kid, from the looks of him, couldn't have been a day over thirteen years old, and at most 89 pounds – dripping wet. He had a cute and sensitive face, and seemed like the kind of kid you'd hire to take in your garbage cans once a week just to avoid buying the obligatory magazine subscriptions that cute kids like that invariably push on you.

But this kid, Ice, even though there was a good chance he'd have one ear permanently stretched to twice the size of the other, didn't come in whimpering or gearing up for a nice healthy thirteen-year-old tantrum. He was silent. Big soulful eyes staring up at me like those pictures of puppies they put on the cover of the dog adoption brochures.

Now, put yourself in my shoes for a second. I mean, come on. Aren't you, just as I was, really intrigued about what this dynamic duo could possibly be doing in this room more commonly utilized to eradicate feminine pubic hair and facial wrinkles?

Sure, I flashed on the thought that the kid might have a birthmark or something –but a loving dad who wants his offspring to be free of an unsightly blemish doesn't usually transport the child by way of the earlobe.

It didn't take long for the story to unfold. Without much ceremony, the father lifts up the kid's shirt, showing me Ice's back. What's there? Only the most humongous tattoo I have ever seen, featuring the letters "A. P." These letters cover the kid's entire back, which while I admit is not a huge back, still adds up to a pretty massive tat.

I'm tempted to tell this story in a way that makes me look a little less out of touch with the times, but by now you're probably not thinking of me as the sharpest knife in the drawer anyway. I see the "A.P." tattoo and immediately find the kid even cuter than ever. Geez, I figure if a kid is a good enough student to put "A.P." on his back – like A.P. English or Calculus, I figure – he's gotta be a pretty cool young man.

Or maybe, I muse, these are his initials. Oh, or more likely, those of a neighborhood girlfriend. Sure! That would explain the earlobe abuse: son gets huge crush on girl down the street. To prove his undying love for her he, unknown to Mom and grim-faced Dad, gets a tattoo the size of a Buick with her initials.

At this moment, even though the possibility of this story being true indicates the kid might be a bit on the noodle-headed side, it still suggests a certain romanticism not usually found in post-puberty males anywhere west of Omaha, Nebraska.

But my benefit-of-the-doubt fantasy is quickly dashed on the rocks of reality when Daddy Warbutt informs me that "A.P." is a gang symbol meaning Armenian Power. Now, I don't claim to know a whole lot about gangs – but it never occurred to me that Muppet-like kids with faces (and ears, apparently) that you want to pinch were the kind of recruits to whom gangs would offer membership.

And "Armenian Power"? I don't know, I just always thought of gang members as a lot of other things, but Armenian?!!! Well, that just tells me how far out of the loop I must truly be. Shoot, what do I know about Armenia? I know they have great bread. Okay, now I know they also have really cute thugs. Clueless, huh?

But hey, there's no need for the kid or his stonefaced father to know just how unhip I really am. I simply nod gravely, shooting the kid a glance, as if to say, "Yeah, I know it's a jungle out there, Homey." (Wow, I can add that to the list of things I never thought I'd accomplish in this lifetime. What were the odds I would ever in my life correctly use the word "homey" in a legitimate sentence? Even if I never get to Mt. McKinley, I can still say I conquered the "H" word.)

Besides, I've had some experience with gangs before. In fact, with gangs and tattoos. I was part of one of the initial pilot programs offering tattoo removal to gang members who wanted to break free from their former destructive lifestyles. For many of these toughs, getting rid of the insignia represented the first step in finalizing their break with the gang lifestyle. The program provided my services free of charge to those who participated, and was sponsored by the local police department. The applicants had to have been free of gang activity, and not been arrested within one year of treatment. They also had to put in a decent number of community service hours, I guess to prove their sincerity about turning their lives around. And the truth is, most of the patients I met were real standup guys. Some of them had small tats, like a teardrop above one cheek, while others were covered in ink. They ranged in age, but none seemed as young and wet behind the ears as the nearly one-eared kid whom I find before me today.

Looking at the massive letters on the little boy's back, I stifle a giggle – not because of how it looks, but because I cannot stop picturing what this little guy's "What I Did This Summer" essay at school must have been like. "Uh, yeah, I went with some friends and had a tattoo etched into the skin of my entire back. Oh, and we also, you know, gang-banged a little. Yo, South Armenia is in the hiz-ouse."

The dad, however, has no trace of a grin on his face. He announces in no uncertain terms that he wants this tattoo gone in sixty seconds. The kid, of course, stares at the floor. Betraying only the smallest crack in the armor of his emotions, the father looks at his child, shakes his head, and mutters, "Can you imagine? He's thirteen!"

Unfortunately for Daddio, I am not in the mood or the zone to gift him even the slightest empathy. This whole situation is kinda weirding me out, and I sense it's only gonna get worse when I give this pair the hard facts about tattoos.

See, tattoos are complicated. As you probably know, there's a whole meticulous process that goes into applying them. Well folks, that ain't nothin' compared to the process of getting them off. So, the cost factor is pretty steep. If it costs, say, fifty dollars to have a tattoo applied, it's gonna cost around $5,000 to get it removed. Well, Ice's tat was no fifty dollar jobby. I mean, a drawing the size of the state of New Hampshire is no small task. I don't know a whole lot about gangland economics, so who knows what Ice had to pay or do to proclaim his allegiance to Armenia and gangsters everywhere, but now I have to drop the bomb on his pop that removing these particular initials from this particular back is gonna be in the fifty thousand dollar range. So, the dad starts to look like he himself is about to give birth to a second son right on the floor of my treatment room, while the kid remains eerily silent. I continue to inform them that even if they want to pay the king's ransom, I couldn't possibly remove the whole thing in one, or even ten, sessions.

You can't give a patient that large a dose of Lidocaine®, the chemical we use in tattoo removal. Lidocaine® is the drug they give patients to restart the heart, so obviously, I'm not gonna pump a massive dose of it into a thirteen-year-old kid no matter how many forty-ounce beers he has illegally consumed with his buddies.

Ever the voice of compassion and care, the father asks, "Can you just sand it off?"

Sand it off. I want to ask, "Sir, is your name Gipetto? Sure, just leave little Pinocchio with me, and we'll have him good as new, as soon as I can plug in my Black and Decker."

Finally the father insists I just do whatever I can in fifteen minutes. But, he decrees, there is to be no numbing. That's his idea of a just punishment for his son. Whatever. Before I can do any work, I have to get an okay from the son – we're not in the Stone Age any more – and the kid just nods his head.

So, as I go to work on a small area of the tattoo, my new hero never makes a sound, and never flinches – not once. I have had people pass out, scream and cry, but not this kid. He was not going to show one ounce of pain. I guess he didn't want to give his father the satisfaction of seeing his pain. Or maybe he was just that tough. That's why I call him "Ice." The kid had ice water in his veins.

I never saw either of them again.

The Moth and the Flame

It takes all kinds. I keep telling myself that. Especially on days where the eccentricities of my clientele begin to make me question whether I am still on planet Earth, or have fallen through some tiny crack in the time-space continuum. And what is it about three in the morning? Is that some universally agreed-upon time for all living beings to obsess about their appearance and dial my phone number? Or was there a nationwide memo sent out that I didn't receive, and I'm the only person still actually sleeping at three a.m.? And is this really the hour to inform me that one of your eyes looks larger than the other? Does it really seem like I have the power to do anything about that? In the next fifteen minutes? This revelation cannot wait until at least more than two of my brain cells are actually functioning? Even if I *could* do something about this horrible discovery, which I empathize to be a source of great embarrassment when you are under public scrutiny. But who is going to see you between now and the normal waking hours of this society? The way I see it, anybody who lays eyes on you at this hour is either too sleepy or too wasted to even notice the fine details that are pushing you slowly off the cliff of sanity.

But I try not to judge. In truth, if I weren't an R.N. with the ability to perform the services I need on my own body, I'd probably be ringing someone's cell phone at all hours of the night, too. Mr. Insecurity has no office hours. He's like a 7/11 for neurosis, and he's open for business round the clock. Plus, I can't really totally put myself in the shoes of my clients. Most of them are celebrities, which I am not. A large number are filthy rich, which I totally, emphatically am not. And many of them are crazy, which I – well, the votes still aren't in.

But some patients take the fanaticism to a whole new extreme. Put yourself in my shoes. How would you handle it?

2 p.m. Tuesday:

I am hard at work on a particularly jammed day when suddenly I hear shouting coming from the reception area of the spa. Now, the last thing a patient who has a hypodermic needle being inserted centimeters from her left eyeball wants to hear is a whole lot of commotion and distraction. I excuse myself briefly from the session, stepping out to the lobby to see what's up. What I find is a client, one of our better-known local news anchors, shouting at the receptionist that she must see Jamie. I overhear the receptionist telling her that today is a particularly packed schedule, and Miss Our-Top-Story-for-Tonight is nowhere on that schedule. At which point Miss OTSFT begins yelling "Do you know who I am"? Well, of course we know who she is. But in a place where Miss Recent Oscar Winner, Mr.-World-Class-Just-Signed–a-New-Multimillion-Dollar-Contract Athlete, and Mrs. Married-to-One-of-the-World's-Most-Powerful-Men are right down the hall, it feels a little over-the-top for a local newscaster to be playing the "I'm too important to be trifled with" card. Besides, when you're a client of this spa, your importance is assumed. What, you think at these prices, we're dissing you because we don't think you're important? Hell, everybody in here is important.

Unfortunately, as I ponder this, Miss OTSFT spots me out of the corner of her eye and comes charging over. But this time with all smiles. Lot's of "Hiiiiii Jaaaaamie"'s and "Look at you, you look greaaaaat"'s. But before long she cuts to the chase. She's going on the air in a couple of hours and has a small "issue" on her face that just has to be taken care of immediately. When I remind her that my schedule is totally packed, but I can see her as soon as possible later in the week, she starts to come unglued, repeating, "But I go on the air in a couple of hours!"

Here's why I have a receptionist. See, because I understand. I can't help but feel for her because I wouldn't want to go on the air either if there was some part of my face that all I could think about was a million people staring at and clucking their tongues. As Bill Clinton would say, "I feel her pain." But on this particular day there really is nothing I can do, short of shafting some other most-important-in-her-own-world patient.

When I tell her exactly that, she begins to follow me around the facility like your kid brother used to do when you were going somewhere cool that he wasn't invited. And I don't mean just following. I mean on my heels, in my face every step – for a long time. She now reminds me of Bill Murray in that movie *What About Bob?* when his shrink refuses to see him and he shouts, "Gimme, gimme, gimme. I need, I need, I neeeeeeeed!" In a matter of hours, the metropolitan Los Angeles area will tune in to hang on this woman's every word, but for now she's behaving like a cocker spaniel that thinks I have Bacon Bits in my pocket.

As you can guess, I cannot resume my work with my new shadow dogging my every step, and after a while it gets just plain ridiculous. So now, I have only two choices. I can call for Security to drag her out kicking and clawing while she screams, "Does anyone realize just who I am?" Or I can do the thing I hate to do, but which usually works: speak to her in a tone normally reserved for her mother.

"Young woman, this is completely unacceptable! Now you get a grip on yourself this instant! The issue in question is easily concealable for today's telecast, and I suggest you use what little time you have to huddle with your network makeup artist to devise a plan to do just that. In the meantime, do not embarrass yourself by shouting and whining like a petulant child." Now the flip: "You are a major star. You must carry yourself as one at all times. We adore you here, and will make every concession to schedule you the most immediate emergency session, and all of your fears will melt away. You will remain the most beautiful woman on the airwaves. Until that time, grab your purse, walk out that front door, and go be the dazzling star that you are. Good day."

As if in a hypnotic trance, she nods and takes her purse and her attitude out the door, not to be seen until the next day when I pull strings to squeeze her in for a treatment. And of course, when I see her, the previous encounter is never mentioned. She is joyous, playful, and a pleasure to be with – as if the day before had never happened. It takes all kinds.

But there's more.

Thursday, 2 p.m.:

Another busy day in Botox City. I check the schedule just to see what the rest of the day has in store. I notice my next appointment is entered as an emergency rush for a woman who has a Playboy Bunny tattoo on her hip, and needs it removed ASAP. I can't help wondering why a tattoo that has been on your hip for perhaps years would suddenly need emergency removal. But I know that in this world in which I live, lots of things that seem like insanity actually have a perfectly sound explanation. Maybe the girl has a film audition, and she doesn't want to mar her chances to book the innocent ingénue role by revealing the Bunny insignia in the middle of her screen test. Or, more likely, she's been dating a hot new guy for a short while, and she can feel that relationship is about to make a turn for the, shall we say, intimate. Tomorrow night is the night, and she's not ready for all of the questions that will come when Mr. Destiny spots Hugh Hefner's personal signature on his dream girl's hip.

Now, as I told you earlier, tattoo removal, like most of the services I perform, is not an instant thing. You can't just walk in at two with Dennis Rodman's face painted on your neck, and waltz out an hour later wearing a tank top claiming you never heard of the guy. These things take time. And hey, it's none of my business, but my philosophy is, if you're a Bunny, you're a Bunny. If the guy you're thinking of doing the nasty with has a problem with that, what better time to find out about it than *before* you do the dirty deed. That tattoo is almost a divine warning sign reading: proceed at your own risk. Most guys I've known would shift into fourth gear and hit the accelerator.

But of course I am prepared to do everything I can to help the damsel in distress. That's what I do. And it's not a bit unusual for me to be working with Bunny types. Think about it: what women on this planet would be more motivated to preserve their youthfulness and beauty than those who make their living being photographed in various states of dress and undress? The window of opportunity for these gals is so small you can't fit a standard air conditioner in it. And it only takes one sagging jowl to slam that window shut tighter than – well, enough metaphors on that subject. Let's just say I'm not a hater when it comes to the Bunnies. They go from treatment to treatment trying to stretch the lease on that room at the mansion, and I'm there for them.

Just recently I worked with Miss My-Favorite-Month-of-the-Year, in the Year-of-(I think)-the-chicken. She wanted one-stop shopping, so she was at my office bright and early twice a week for a good while. She got the works. Botox on her forehead and around both eyes. A Restylane® filler under both eyes (Restylane® is a relatively new alternative to collagen, the bovine-based epidermal filler; with a couple of treatments, dark circles and "crater face" are things of the past). She also wanted the Aluma electrothermal skin tightening treatment, which is a wonderful alternative to the facelift process. I took enough hair off different parts of her body to weave an afghan. And once her body was hairless and smooth, I gave her a series of mesotherapy injections, the same process that allowed Ms. Legendary-Solo-Singer-and-Earthy-Diva to lose a whopping forty pounds. I couldn't help wondering if, when her centerfold came out, the guys fantasizing about her could handle these sessions as a part of the picture.

I also do a lot of work for other working women whose looks are the key to their longevity. Since your minds probably have already dropped down south, I'll admit, I have several hooker clients. Give me a break. If that was how you made your living wouldn't you use a portion of the considerable cash you're raking in to protect your investment by losing that peach fuzz on your back? That's called recycling.

There are a couple of other services that are requested by people in these lines of work more often than other clients. The first, G-spot injection, is a service I don't perform. It involves injecting a filler into the G-spot, making it easier to find. Logically, when that blessed spot is easier to locate, climax is more likely. I personally prefer to let my partner search for it. Half the fun is in the hunt. Hey, whatever happened to foreplay? But I don't judge. I just farm this work out to a doctor in Beverly Hills who thinks that kind of stuff is really interesting. We've had so many requests for a service called anal bleaching that we now offer it. Anal bleaching is exactly what it sounds like, and is most often requested by exotic dancers, porn stars, and other professionals whose occupation requires that others view your anus. I'll let you ponder what those professions might be. I think you'd be surprised, though, how many everyday people request this service. And if you want it, I have no problem performing the treatment. Who am I to dictate what color anyone's anus should be, porn star, prostitute or banker?

But I was really referring to actresses and housewives. Having dabbled in acting, I know how ruthless Hollywood can be to a young woman who has let even one part of her body get a little out-of-standard-perfection range. I have a casting director who keeps a stack of my business cards in his desk. When he meets a talented actress who has slipped south of a perfect ten, he closes his door, and whispers in her ear, "Honey, you're starting to look thirty. Take this card, and I'll see you in six weeks." And most of them do exactly what the reluctant Bunny has done – show up at nurse Jamie's office.

She arrived at two o'clock on the dot. How can I say this? Summoning every ounce of tact I have ever had the good fortune to acquire, I must say: George Foreman could be a Bunny sooner than this woman. If you stood her and George Washington, the father of our country, on a stage, announcing that one of these two has a Bunny tattoo, when the drawers were dropped, you'd be checking out George to see where he put the tat.

So, although I can't imagine how or why the tattoo got there, or why it's so urgent to get it off, I'm going to use everything in my creative power to bring her wishes to fruition.

We enter the treatment room where it's necessary for her to disrobe, the sight of which makes the Bunny tat all the more incongruous. But if girlfriend has the stuff to wear it, I have the stuff to remove it. We begin the laser treatment, and I am very careful to make sure she is relatively comfortable every step of the way. She reassures me each time that she is fine, though I suspect she's having second thoughts.

As I may have mentioned before, the process of getting a tattoo is a relatively painful one, as the ink is inserted into your skin through a series of needle jabs, which eventually scab over. When the scab falls away, *voila*, hello tattoo. Well, the process to remove that same tattoo is considerably more painful, as the laser blasts the pigment into smaller particles in the epidermal layer so that the white blood cells can readily carry away the fragmented pigment. So I want to be sure that this woman, who doesn't look like a thrill seeker or a wild child, can handle the process. But she smiles and chirps, "I'm just fine."

Because the Bunny logo is small, the session is quick, and the Reluctant Bunny is pleased. I walk her to the front counter to schedule a follow-up appointment. She smiles gratefully as I turn to glance at the appointment book. When I look back, she is gone. In one second she has vanished. I look down. . . there she is, out cold on the hard tile floor. It takes all kinds.

But that's nothing compared to:

Friday, 10 a.m.:

I call this freaky Friday. Not every Friday is freaky Friday. Only when The-Moth-Who-Would-Be-Butterfly is coming in. Let me state for the record, I love The Moth. She is a delightful woman who is kind and considerate. She has a good job and a beautiful family whom she adores. She loves her husband so much that her mission has become to stay as young and lovely as she can to keep the fires of passion burning. She truly is not particularly vain. She just wants her man to feel like he picked a winner no matter how long they are together.

Appointments with The Moth are completely reliable. You can set your watch by them. There are very few things in this life that you can truly count on. Among those are death, taxes, and The Moth. Every sixth Friday the Moth makes her way to my office as if drawn in the same way a salmon fights its way upstream. And freaky Friday is underway.

What makes it freaky is the unchanging routine. Like clockwork the front door will swing open for a smiling Moth who makes pleasant chatter while distributing small but thoughtful gifts to the office staff. After some juicy gossip and pleasantries all around, she makes her way into the treatment room where she carefully places what are usually a brand new and fashionable pair of shoes beneath the treatment table before she cheerfully climbs up to begin the session. At the first application of my laser or a needle, she immediately faints dead away, urinating all over herself and often falling off the table.

Some minutes later she groggily awakens, apologizes profusely, continues the session, and makes her way home in wet pants on shaky legs. Six weeks later she is back like a moth to a flame to repeat the exact same process. The *exact* same!

I've said it before, but it bears repeating: it takes all kinds!

Genesis

Sunday, 4 a.m.

Date: Classified

It is completely fitting that I should be born on a day of rest at this ungodly hour. Maybe it's a fitting payback that my life is now a never-ending series of calls from the rich, famous and vain needing my services, my advice or just my sympathy at times when any right-thinking person would be fast asleep.

What doesn't quite fit is that I grew up in, of all places, a thirty-acre cattle farm in a totally obscure part of Indiana, a town called Kurtz, population (are you ready?) twenty-two. Okay, twenty-three. I am the third child, my parents' third daughter. My two sisters are sixteen and fourteen years older, so I'm thinking I may have come as somewhat of a surprise. Because of the huge age gap between me and my sisters, I grew up pretty much like an only child, learning to become extremely independent from the very beginning.

Now that I live in Los Angeles, thirty acres seems like a huge property; but in our little part of Indiana, that's a drop in the bucket. Our tiny farm was still about two miles from the nearest neighbor. As you can guess, there wasn't a whole lot of bicycle riding as a means of transportation. It didn't take me long to learn to ride one of our family dirtbikes, and at a very tender age I claimed my independence by taking off for the nearest neighbor's farm, where my friend Stephanie and I would hang out together. If we were feeling adventurous, Stephanie would let me talk her into revving up our mopeds and heading for Indianapolis, which was about an hour ride away. Imagine the sight of these two young girls buzzing into the big city on these two scooters. You gotta love it!

As I grew up, it became more and more natural for me to strike out on my own and discover new things and new people. I was always a tall kid, so I looked very mature for my age. I was five-foot-eight as a high school freshman, and by my fifteenth birthday I had reached five-ten. People always thought I was older, and I certainly didn't mind them thinking that if it allowed me some new wild adventures.

I think a lot of this wild independent spirit was made possible by the fact that my mom, after already raising my two sisters, was just plain worn out. She was pretty much "over" the kid thing, and certainly didn't have the energy to go chasing me down as I set out on my various adventures. At age fifteen I decided I just had to attend a Kiss concert with some friends I had met on a secret excursion to Cincinnati. I told my mom I was sleeping over at a local friend's house. Of course that was fine with her, to have me out of her hair for a night, and as soon as I left the house, I was off to the bus station bound for Ohio, a rendezvous with my buddies, and a connecting bus to Tennessee. That's just the way I rolled. If there was a place I wanted to go, or something I wanted to do, I just went for it.

At my school, which was a one- to three-hour bus ride, depending on what road was washed out or snowed under, I was popular enough, even though I was kind of a loner and a rebel. In the eighth grade, one of the senior boys asked me to the senior prom, which felt like a true honor to me. My mom, on the other hand, didn't see it that way, and refused to let me go with him. No problem – just being asked made me feel like the Homecoming Queen. I actually made cheerleader in my freshman year, and would really have gotten into it if I hadn't had so many other adventures going on at the same time.

Because of my height and mature attitude, I was always making older friends. I would go to lots of college parties where I met lots of cool college students. One of these friends was a female who attended Ball State and had her own apartment. She kind of resembled me, so she let me use her phone bill and vital statistics to get a fake I.D. Now I had the freedom to really conquer new territory. I would go to bars in the city and hang with the really happening people. I didn't drink alcohol, and still don't to this day. I just wanted to meet cute guys, and these big-city bars were a far better shot for that than the Kurtz ice cream social.

So you could say I got kind of wild. I didn't really do anything my parents wouldn't have approved of, but I found myself attending classes less and less, until finally I had exceeded the limit for absences. This meant I was in danger of being held back a year in school. Lucky for me, my dad was a member of the school board. The combination of his influence, and the fact that I was actually a pretty good student who just wasn't challenged by the classes (I had a B+ average), and my Mamaw (Grandmother) always covering for me by writing "please excuse" notes when I needed them, kept me on track to graduate on time.

But my mind had left Kurtz long before. I mean, in a school where my graduating class was eighty-nine students, there just wasn't enough excitement or opportunity to satisfy my soul.

So, that's when I began my obsession with Ball State. I wanted to go there so bad, it was all I could talk and think about from the time I was a sophomore. Every chance I got I was hanging with Ball State students, visiting the campus, and reading anything I could find about it. I ended up not going to my own junior or senior prom, simply because, in my mind, I had already moved on to Ball State. I chattered about it so incessantly that I remember my mom once saying to me, "If you say the name Ball State one more time, I'm going to whack you across the face!" It probably still didn't stop me. I had Ball State on the brain.

The positive part of this was that as I got closer to my senior year, I began attending and working harder in my classes, just so I could qualify for – you know what – Ball State. Finally after what seemed like an eternity, I graduated high school, was accepted at my dream college, and packed up to set out for the big city: Muncie!

I guess you're getting the picture of how tiny Kurtz, Indiana really is. I mean, when Muncie starts feeling like a huge metropolis, you can bet Kurtz is truly a mere speck on the hole in the wall of life.

The truth is, as soon as I got to school in Muncie, I started looking for bigger and better things. That's just my way. I wanted to work so I would have cash to do the things I wanted to do, so I began checking my options. I knew I could probably waitress at any one of the local bars where they had known me for years now. But I was already thinking I didn't want to get stuck as a Muncie girl, so it seemed like the perfect opportunity when I found out the airlines were hiring flight attendants. Oh yeah! Travel, insurance, cash? Where do I sign up? But my parents felt very strongly that I shouldn't have such a distracting job while I was in school. I wonder where they got the idea that I could be distracted from my studies. So as a compromise, I promised them I would wait until the summer, when they had a six-week SSP (Summer Support Program), which was a crash (pardon the pun) course for summer flight attendants.

I passed that course with flying (pardon the other pun) colors, and became a part-time employee.

It all happened so fast I could hardly believe it when I was assigned my first flight: Guantanamo Bay, Cuba. I was so excited, feeling like a true adult for the first time in my life. When we checked into our crew hotel in Florida for the layover, (citizens were not allowed to stay over in Cuba) I realized it was the first hotel stay of my life without my parents. I danced around my room like a little kid on Christmas morning.

Maybe I wasn't such a grownup after all. Hanging up my flight attendant uniform, I caught a glimpse of myself in the mirror, so far from that girl on a moped buzzing along the back roads of Kurtz. And yet, so much to learn, and so far still to go.

Undercover with
Hollywood Royalty

Friday, 9 p.m.:

Once again everyone else in the sane world is either out on a date or rocking it in some bar, getting ready to land the big one. I, however, as Mayor of Botox City, will have none of that. Why should I have a life when there are desperate celebrities out there on the precipice of showing their age? How could I possibly answer the Batphone, slip into my leotard and cape, and save the day (or at least the skin), if I am actually somewhere having a life?

So here I am, actually able to answer the phone on the first ring when I get "the call." I do not recognize the voice on the other end of the line because there is no voice. I do recognize the silence. I know who it is, and I know what is next. It is the B.O.S.S. No, not Bruce, the music superstar. It's the B.O.S.S., the Box Office Super Star. The routine is almost comical, except the B.O.S.S. is not kidding.

"What time do you open in the morning?" he begins. With the requisite pause where I *could* but *do not* speak, he continues. "Ten? That'll be great." I do not say a word. He continues. "Thank you very much."

I partly expect the theme from *Mission: Impossible* to begin playing as I choose photographs of the team I will assemble to pull off some espionage caper. But there is no music, and I am really going alone to do a house call treatment. Ten is the signal for a ten p.m. appointment at the home of Box Office Super Star and his wife.

What would normally be a simple procedure is raised to a supreme level of drama by the mere fact that this sizzling film star and his wife need my services, but do not under any circumstances want their children to know that they have Botox treatments. I mean, I'm used to sneaking around to hide the work I do from the press and from my clients' fans, but this concept of creating the grand illusion inside the B.O.S.S.'s own home is a new level of absurdity. But, as Mayor of Botox City, my job is not to question, but to don my secret agent disguise and complete the mission.

The disguise, in truth, is really just a question in this case of not wearing scrubs or anything that might make me look like a medical practitioner. A skirt and heels would do the trick, but I'll be damned if I'm gonna teeter around the B.O.S.S.'s house on pumps trying to administer a Botox injection with my feet screaming bloody murder. So, jeans and a sweatshirt with a cute cap will have to do. See, the play is, I'm a girlfriend of the B.O.S.S.'s wife, who comes over to gossip and borrow clothes. I need to do the jeans-and-tennis-shoes thing because I know that the couple wants "the works" this visit, which means I'll be needing a lot of supplies which I'll have to conceal in a backpack. I load up the denim backpack with vials of all of the goodies I'll need to do the minor stuff like skin peels, and a small portable laser for treatment of pigmentation and broken facial blood vessels, and any other minor stuff that can be done outside the office. I toss in a couple of other tools of the trade and head for the door.

Something about this mission of insanity makes me want to check my rear view mirror to see if I am being tailed. It's just more fun that way, since there is absolutely zero chance that anybody on this green earth gives a rat's ass where I am going at this moment.

When I arrive at the house, the odyssey builds in its strangeness. See, the children that this entire masquerade has been created to deceive, are teenagers. It's not like there are a couple of toddlers whose psyches would be scarred by the knowledge that their parents are clinging to their missing-but-not-lost youth. But the B.O.S.S. is the boss, and I have no life anyway. If I weren't here I'd be at some other mansion playing out some other absurd scene.

I have to be careful not to let on how heavy my backpack really is, even though the weight of it is doing a number on my lower back. I've had to pack it extra full because once I'm inside the house, I'll be working not only on the Hollywood power couple, but on most of their staff as well. There's the woman who runs the house, a job I never knew existed until my election as Mayor. She's going to have a couple of things done while I'm here. There's the housekeeper, who needs a Juvéderm treatment, and the Gulf Stream pilot who will have a little of this and a little of that, and the personal flight attendant who, like the two family friends who appear from nowhere, prefers anything that works fast and makes her look and feel *younger*. Fine.

Now while I'm doing all of this I have to somehow get them behind closed doors while we do a sort of improvisational chatter to lend the illusion of us just hanging out and shooting the breeze simply for the benefit of any of the teenagers who might be within earshot. As if any teenager on the face of this earth would give two cents to hear anything their parents and the parents' friends have to say.

After all of this, the man of the house gets the full treatment.

He has been a client for a long time – so long, in fact, that he no longer asks for specific services. He trusts my judgment because he knows the work I do will be tasteful and scarcely noticeable. If I say he needs some work on forehead lines, or a little mesotherapy on the love handles that The Zone Delivery and two personal trainers couldn't remove, many of the answers lie in my backpack full of goodies. But it gets more complicated. See, to do Botox or any of the stuff that requires the equipment in my office and the supervision of our staff M.D., I've now got to do this major improvisation about how we're all going to go out for gelato or something, so I can load all the adults in the car and we can meet up at the office and protect the future of America's box-office, as well as the future of those who run his empire.

And please tell me, how stupid are we thinking these kids are? Seriously, do other parents load the housekeeper, the nanny, the mechanic, and the stable boy into the car to hunt for gelato at some ungodly hour? I don't know a kid on this planet who wouldn't be like, "Yeah right." But mine is not to question why. I am the Mayor, and these are my people. So, if it ends up like a cross between *MacGyver* and *Flatliners*, I'm down with it. Shimmy through a window to make my escape unnoticed? You betcha!

I can only whisper a quick prayer of thanks that I chose the jeans and tennis shoes for this undercover marathon.

 Errors and Omissions

As you may have guessed, I've learned a whole lot about the human body and human skin, the body's largest organ. Part of what makes my clients feel so secure about trusting me with their looks (which for many of them is the same thing as their livelihood) is the fact that I'm not just some stylist with a hypodermic in my hand. Being a registered nurse is serious business, and every procedure I perform is done with the strictest medical guidelines in place.

The only resistance I get is probably due to my appearance. I guess being blonde and Botoxed doesn't inspire a whole lot of confidence that I know a whole lot about medicine. But who says you have to be a prune-faced battleaxe with a rear end as wide as the bumper of a Peterbilt truck to understand and employ the basic principals of medical science? On the contrary, I would think that if I were looking for someone to stick needles in my face, it would have to be someone who knows how it feels to be on the receiving end of the hypodermic. And I would want it to be someone who gets how important it is not just to look good, but to look *flawless.* I've met lots of qualified physicians in my time, men and women whom I would trust completely to remove my appendix or put a splint on a finger. But I'm not letting these characters get anywhere near my eyebrows! I mean, come on! Maybe I could live with a crooked scar just below my ribs, but no way would I survive having one of my eyebrows look like it was drawn on by a fifth grade student. Heck, I can buy a bathing suit that covers my midsection to get past those rare occasions when anybody except my husband might get a glimpse of my torso, but I can't go around with a pillowcase over my head to conceal a faulty lip augmentation. Everybody sees your face, and let's be honest, as kind and empathetic as any of us may be, there's something grossly unforgettable about an otherwise pretty girl with a lip that looks like she lost a ten-rounder with George Foreman.

So any day of the week I want my cosmetic practitioner to be someone who has a sense of style, and some integrity about the work he or she does. It would be like going to a beauty salon to have a guy who looks like boxing promoter Don King work on your hair. Dude, if you think that rat's nest on top of your head looks good, what on earth will you do with *my* hair?

And who would have more sense of style about the minute details that enhance a woman's or man's appearance than someone who doesn't settle for less in her or his own appearance? Why do you think so many of the stars choose a gay stylist? Be reasonable. It has nothing to do with the sexuality. It has to do with the meticulous attention many (but not all) gay men give to appearance and style. Well, I'm not a guy, and my husband will testify that I'm straight, but I'm your best bet if you want some work done on a body part that people will see.

My philosophy is pretty simple: I'm similar, in a way, to a film director. If you're noticing my work when you view the finished product, then I haven't done my job. If you're a client of mine, I don't want people walking up to you saying, "Ooooh, looks like somebody got a little Botox! Nice job!" The enhancements I do should be just that: enhancements, procedures that make you look better without becoming the object of everyone's attention. And so my outlook is simple: I won't do any work on you that I wouldn't be happy walking around with on my own face or body. And believe me, when it comes to my own appearance, I'm the town's toughest critic.

So I have studied extremely hard to know what I'm doing. I'm constantly taking the latest seminar on the latest technique or equipment. And I'm always studying the human face and body. Forgive me if I meet you at a party and you see me staring you down. There's no problem or hidden grudge. I'm just looking at that tiny wrinkle on your forehead, thinking how I could make it disappear without making you look like you suffered a minor stroke on that side of your face. And with each person I study, my technique and my creative approach get stronger.

But I gotta admit, I wasn't always the sharpest tool in the shed. I've made my share of stupid mistakes and erroneous conclusions. Let me flip a few pages back in my diary to give you a couple of examples.
..

It is three weeks after my twentieth birthday, and aside from the usual early twenties' issues of desperate finances, serious questions about what to really do with one's life, whom to spend your life with, and how to acquire a car you can afford that actually runs and makes hot guys check you out at the same time, life is rosy.

Unfortunately, my complexion is not. It must be some cruel joke of nature that a person like me whose entire life has been dedicated to dermal perfection would be among the ranks of those who suffer prepubescent acne well after the period in which you care about who made the cheer squad or incessantly use words like "like" as an adjective. You don't have to be a cosmetic surgeon or a beauty fanatic to hate the sight of skin that resembles a thin-crust sausage pizza. Well, that was me well into my twenties, and as you can guess, I wasn't in the mood to sit still for that.

I had been seeing a really good dermatologist to treat my acne for some time. He would concentrate on any cystic nodules I might have by zapping them with a shot of cortisone. What's a cystic nodule, you ask? Well, think of it as a huge zit that just won't go away no matter how much squeezing and popping you attempt – and if you have my luck, it is usually positioned right smack in the middle of your forehead or on the tip of your nose, kinda like a neon sign that flashes "UNDESIRABLE" to anyone who comes within fifteen feet of you. So, this derm would give me a couple of quick shots of cortisone, and the offending pimple would head for the hills until the next month or until I scheduled an important date, whichever came first.

Cortizone injections actually work really well on cystic nodules – that is, unless you inject too much. But this derm was pretty good at his craft, so I had never had any problems. The saying tends to be true: there's a first time for everything. On this particular day, I had the usual injections. I don't know if the doctor injected too much, or if the solution was not diluted enough, but either way I found that the zit, while disappearing, went down a little *too far,* leaving me with a small depression in the center of my forehead which looked like someone had whacked me upside the head with a ball-peen hammer, which is an okay look for a bathroom wall that's being drywalled, but not so hot for a red-blooded blonde in the middle of her sexual prime. If you didn't stare too closely, it looked as if I had an aggravated case of cellulite between my eyebrows. This small depression on my face led to a major depression of my soul, which *had* to be dealt with. I called the derm who gave me the injection, and his response was that I should give it time and it would in all likelihood return to normal. Yeah right. Like I'm gonna walk around with a hole in my head looking like a front-end forceps baby. What should I do when some cute guy starts looking at me like I was created in a laboratory? Give him a note from my doctor?

So I immediately got to work conjuring up solutions to this earth-shattering issue. It didn't take long for me to come up with what at the time appeared to be sheer genius, as do many things at the wise and invincible age of twenty. It's like having the name of your summer camp counselor tattooed onto your neck because he's so cool, so brilliant, and you never want to forget him. Brilliant.

My newest stroke of genius was to have a plastic surgeon friend liposuction some fat out of my ass and re-inject it into the crater in my forehead filling the "human Grand Canyon." Pretty inspired thinking if you really consider it. I mean, goodness knows I have plenty of available fat on my fanny, it comes from my own body – so there's no problem with tissue match – and besides, my friends have always called me a butthead, so now it would actually have some factual authenticity. Sounded like baby Einstein stuff to me.

I figured while I was at it, I should have some lipo done on my thighs and the rest of my booty. Keep in mind I was actually pretty darned thin at the time, but when do thinner thighs and a smaller bum ever sound like a bad idea to a twenty-year-old? So, my brilliant idea began to seem like a sure thing to make me a Rhodes Scholar! Two birds with one stone. So we set the plan in motion.

Let me pause here for a moment to speak about liposuction. Medically speaking, it sucks. Of all the procedures I have had done, and I have pretty much had them all, liposuction is the one I regret. Which do I regret more, cutting off my left pigtail at age six or liposuction? No contest. I'd gladly give up both pigtails and my bangs for the chance to rethink that first lipo. I'd even kiss Morris Zlotnik again, even without the assistance of the six sloe gin fizzes, before I'd agree to another lipo treatment. I confess the technology of liposuction has come a long way in the past ten or fifteen years, but even with all of that you couldn't convince me to lie down on that table again. Seriously, it's just a primitive process, and flat-out too hard to control the look of the results. After my first session my legs looked like a sack of potatoes. I must remind you, we're talking about a thin and fit twenty-year-old who is obsessed with keeping up her appearance. Suddenly one of my best assets looks like the arms of Lucy's friend Ethel Mertz.

I couldn't believe it. The guy who did the procedure looked at my legs and said, "I've seen worse." Well, *that's* reassuring. And I'm sure my dentist has treated some ninety-year-old lifetime boozers who have only one rotted tooth left in their heads – but that doesn't mean I should hang onto the single cavity in my upper left molar. Of course he's seen worse!

Since that fateful day I have had two corrective surgeries to try to make my legs look like I am a carbon-based creature rather than a being from the planet Myanus. Of course when people hear that I have had three liposuctions, they expect my legs to be really thin and shapely. Well, I hate to disappoint them, but I'm settling just to not have them look like a plate of French's instant mashed potato buds. Now that the technology of mesotherapy injections has been developed, there's a good chance I'll someday reintroduce short pants to my wardrobe, but don't bet on it. The scars on my ego might be too deep. But at least when I get totally wrung out about my legs, I can take comfort in the fact that I wasn't a victim to some quack stranger. No, the idea was all mine.

As for the hole in my head: well, that's an even better story. We filled the gap with my butt fat, and it looked really good. I figured that might make up for the less-than-stellar lipo idea. At least I was batting .500, which would make me the star of any major league baseball team (except the Yankees).

Small problem: the fat that fills the gap was harvested from my buttock and thigh area, a part of my body that tends to swell during my menstrual period. It's like clockwork. If you see me jogging at the park and my thighs look extra large, you can bet it's that time of the month. Well, I can live with that, I suppose. Imagine my surprise, however, when I found that the fat injected into my forehead does the same thing. So now, along with cramps, one week a month my forehead looks like I bumped into some immovable object. Nothing like a huge organic sign that tells the whole world when you've got your period.

Okay, flip forward a few months and a few pages of my diary. I guess I can't tell you we're moving forward on any I.Q. points, because the next story doesn't make me look any less like a numbskull than the last.

You'd think I'd learn to wait until a procedure is tried and true before I experiment on myself like I'm some laboratory rat in a high school biology class. But I just find the whole enhancement industry so fascinating and useful that I'm like a kid on Christmas morning when I hear about a new application that might improve the way I look.

When I first heard about permanent eyeliner, I thought I had died and gone to heaven. I mean, what's not to like? Here's a procedure that allows you to roll out of bed looking like the makeup artist from Mac is permanently on staff at your house. Perfect eyeliner every morning without having to scrunch up against the bathroom mirror hoping your hand is steady enough that day to draw a straight line across your lower eyelid. And if you miss, it's makeup remover, and back to the proverbial and literal drawing board. Plus, think of the extra sleep you got by not having to drag your tired ass into the john to remove the smudged-up mess you've ended up with for eyes, at the end of a long day of flirting and eyelid-batting.

Permanent eyeliner is basically like a tattoo on your eyelid. It's not makeup, and it behaves the same way a tattoo does – lasts a really long time, although even *it* will fade over the course of several years. Then you can have it touched up and start all over again. Well, I said to myself, "I'm all over that!"

Now, I said I was eager, but don't get the wrong idea. I'm not an idiot, even though one week a month my forehead makes me look like one. I did my research and knew that there were several risks involved in the procedure. I wanted a qualified plastic surgeon to do the work, and I thought it would be a good idea for me to wear corneal protectors. I mean, let me say two words to you: needle, eyeball. Enough said? Bring on the corneal protectors, which are basically metal contact lenses, which keep that pesky needle from skewering my eyeball like those olives that float in a martini glass. I'm totally in favor of that. Think about it: what good is perfect eye makeup if you're tapping around with a white cane behind those huge, honkin' Ray-Ban glasses like Ray Charles used to wear?

So we begin the procedure with me feeling pretty good about the safety precautions I have taken. However, being so preoccupied with the preservation of my corneas has distracted me from asking the real important question: could this very friendly and seemingly capable white upper-class male physician possibly know anything about applying eyeliner? And the answer comes back: FAT CHANCE.

Needless to say, with all good intentions, this doctor has given me the look from Kabuki theater. Kind of a blonde, post-snake Cleopatra. Not the look I'm going for at all. But remember, this is a permanent tattoo Dr. Strangelove has just applied to my eyes. Can you spell PERMANENT? What are my options now? Kill the doctor? Move to Taiwan, apply a permanent tattoo of whiteface and join a Kabuki troop? Or better yet, an ongoing production of *Oedipus Rex*, where in the title role I stab needles into my eyes night after night after night. Perfect.

Well, there's still one option left, which is the one I took: a tattoo removal laser. Sounds ideal, right? Well, almost. You see, when you do a laser that close to a delicate area like the eye, something's gotta give. In my case, it was the eyelashes, which instantly fell out. Once again, not the look I was going for. Will somebody please help me!? As a result, I had to wear false eyelashes for six months until my eyelashes began to – pitifully as they do to this day – crawl their way back into existence.

Do I regret going for the permanent liner? Not at all. What I regret is not doing the procedure myself, instead of trusting a permanent makeup application to a guy whose most artistic handiwork is done with a sand wedge just off the sixteenth green.

Just to give the story a happy ending: when they removed the protective contacts (you know, the ones designed to protect my eyes), they gave me a lovely corneal abrasion, which left me in Eyeball Hell for about a week. Beauty is pain.

Flip forward a few more pages, while we're reading *Jamie's Bloopers and Random Acts of Miscalculation and Impaired Judgment. . .*

When they first started using collagen to make people's lips fuller and more luscious, I figured, even though I have always had very naturally full lips, I should try it out. After all, the strength of my profession is that I don't do work that I wouldn't have done on myself. And, as Angelina Jolie has proven, one can never have lips full enough.

Back then the collagen was a bovine derivative (moooo) and had to be tested before use for allergic reactions. Logically, what goes in cows doesn't always go in people. So, going by the book, I had the doctor I was working with give me an injection on the inner aspect of my underarm, and we waited a week to check for a reaction. Seeing none, we decided it was safe to go ahead with injections into my lips. Get ready world, here comes Angelina Jamie!

May I point out here that the lips are a far more sensitive area than other parts of the body? That's why we kiss on the lips instead of brushing underarms. Well, I can only speak for myself; no one gets near my pits. Needless to say, when we injected the collagen into my lips, they didn't want to play that game, and swelled up in an allergic reaction which gave me the kind of lips Goldie Hawn had in that movie *The First Wives Club*. But mine were for real. . . for three weeks. When the reaction finally wore off, my lips returned to normal, and I learned a lesson I try to pass on to my clients, which often falls on deaf ears: Don't fix it if it ain't broke.

I also have to share with you the difficulties of doing procedures on oneself. Of course, my issue is that there's no one I trust to do the delicate work I want done on my own face and body more than myself. So whenever possible, I try to do the work myself. But there are some areas of the body that are just plain hard to reach while holding a syringe or a laser tool. Over the years, however, I have learned to twist myself into numerous pretzel-like positions to provide access to the beautifying treatments I desire.

One time, just as I was going on the first few dates with the man who is now my husband, I was in the final phases of laser hair removal on my "bikini," a piece of work he had only recently observed for the first time. Needless to say, I was motivated to do a better job than ever on my self-lasering procedure. You understand, the vaginal area is a very sensitive spot. That's why instead of rubbing underarms, we – well, you get what I'm talking about.

So when I began my final treatment, I used lots of numbing cream and began the last meticulous work in some areas that my future husband had managed to reach, but which posed a greater challenge for me and my laser. Undaunted, I completed the procedure using a backhanded grip and my best yoga positions.

Not long after, I was in the shower when I noticed some serious swelling in the same area, followed by some even more serious pain. What the Hell??? I couldn't see the area, but it felt suspiciously like a canker sore. Awwww, crap! I raced across town to my gynecologist, fighting the urge to call my new guy and chew him out. How dare he give me some STD and not own up to it? Instead of calling, I rehearsed several excuses to get myself out of our date for later that night. No thank you, you've given me just about enough already. I can't help thinking what other diseases this "player" might be carrying around waiting to pass on to my hairless goody. I started getting nauseous, and had to pull the car over to decide whether to barf or pass out.

By the time I arrived at my gyno, I was a newly self-avowed feminist. I gave the young male office assistant a withering glance, which told him what a pig he was simply by birthright, and he seemed appropriately chastened.

When I finally climbed into the stirrups in the treatment room, my mood was murderous, and it was my doctor's extreme good fortune to have been born a woman. Dr. Susan took a quick peek, then a deep breath, and announced to me that I had a semi-serious. . . burn! The look on her face seemed to beg the question, "How in the name of all that is holy did you get a burn in there?" Now, I needed a deep breath before verbalizing the explanation. It seems

I had applied so much numbing cream during my laser session that I couldn't feel it when my backhand, upside-down pretzel grip put the laser in direct contact with my skin.

Relieved and embarrassed, I drove straight from Dr. Susan's office to a flower shop, where I disavowed my staunch feminism and began the trek toward my very happy marriage. Whew!

 Errors and Omissions 2

It's around eleven a.m. on a Tuesday morning that started out just like any Tuesday in Botox City; the usual mix of the absurd, the Hollywood pretention, and the downright fun. At this relatively early hour, I've already saved several people from their various cosmetic Waterloos. One of the great parts about the work I do is that it is a process that demands a response – almost always overwhelmingly positive. It's not like, for example, going to the dentist where you endure tremendous agony for an hour, only to walk away seeing no difference in your teeth, even though you know they repaired a small new cavity somewhere inside your head. So you walk away numb, one part due to the Novocaine®, another part due to the hefty bill the girl at the desk placed in your shaky hand, and the last part because you just can't tell the difference from before and after the ordeal. In my business there is undeniably some discomfort, but when you finish the treatment you know you've said goodbye to some unsightly issue that has bugged the crap out of you for a long time. Any suffering you may have experienced is rewarded by the knowledge that those five "billy goat gruff" chin whiskers are a thing of the past. *In* with dark circles under your eyes that resemble a basset hound; *out* with the promise of youthfulness and beauty.

I say "the promise" because it's important to remind every patient that the treatments they receive require a few days to a week to really take effect. Some procedures require multiple treatments with a six-week recovery time in between. So while you can't exactly call it instant gratification, you sure as hell know you're gonna be looking a lot better real soon!

As a result, people tend to leave their appointments feeling really hopeful, happy, and thankful, which isn't exactly the way you'd feel after, let's say, a pap smear. Hey, I'm not saying the two are equal in importance. I'm saying you don't see a lot of women hugging and thanking the nurse with the scraper and the Petri dish. I'm not saying – I'm just saying.

So on this particular Tuesday, the mood in the spa is light and positive. I actually take a moment to reflect on how far I've come in so short a time. "Not bad," I think, "for a hairy girl from a miniscule farm town to be more vital to the biggest stars in Hollywood than any six of the people in their entourage." Of course, I'll never make that Oscar or Emmy speech. Even though I know how grateful my clients are, I know that they would sooner admit to being a pen pal of Adolph Hitler than confess that they've ever even met me. I can handle that. Plus, who wants to be mentioned on worldwide television as the person who "lasered unwanted hairs off my butt"? No thank you.

All is well in my world this Tuesday morning, and it appears destined to continue that way. I have one more appointment, and then I'm off for a much needed and much deserved day of shopping. My final appointment is Food Show Model Girl, a lovely, thin, brunette client who has come back to me because she was so pleased with the work I did removing a rose shaped tattoo from her chest. How does that work that at one point in your life you are so into roses that you think, "I'm gonna have one of these permanently inked into my chest"? And then, I guess, you wake up a year or two later thinking, "Freaking roses!" I mean, for my part, I have trouble thinking of anything I like so much that I want to wear it on my skin for the next thirty years. I love my mom, but I'm just fine carrying pictures of her in my wallet. I don't need her image needled into my inner thigh to announce my love to anyone downwind when I use the ThighMaster at the gym. But hey, to each his or her own. My job is to be there for them when roses are no longer the flower of choice or scorpions don't seem as cute and sexy as they did after three hits of Jägermeister one weekend a few years back.

Food Show Model Girl is a really likeable and friendly client. I feel as though I hardly know her because her style is very quiet while warm. She has returned because, having undergone a treatment for permanent lipliner a short while back, she has decided that the color she chose is too dark red. She first went back to the practitioner who did the work, but naturally they looked at her like she had just escaped from a maximum-security mental institution. You see, permanent makeup, like lipsticks and eyeliners, is pure and simply a *tattoo*. The "makeup" is actually a relatively permanent ink drawing on the desired body part. And you can't simply adjust the color once the work is done. So again it seems like it would be a great idea to make sure you really like the color and the shape before you begin the treatment.

The permanent makeup people told her she'd need to do tattoo removal to strip away the offending color. Then she could go back and have a new color reapplied. I should remind you that the process of applying a tattoo is, to say the least, a painful one. If you're like me – not too fond of needles – a simple blood test at my doctor's office is a bit of an ordeal. Imagine now getting stuck with that same needle a couple of thousand times so you can walk away with a picture of Batman on your ass, or as in this case a pair of deep blood-red lips that never require gloss.

Food Girl wants me to remove the tattoo of her lipstick. I feel it's my duty to remind her of any pain she might have had when she applied the tat. I do this because I know that the lip area has double the nerve synapses of other parts of the body. Yep, that means twice the pain. And if I didn't mention it before, taking a tattoo *off* is far more painful a process than having one applied. Yep, that now means about six times the pain. But I suppose she has asked herself "the awesome question" – which is, of course, "What is more important: having beautiful lips that never smear, or avoiding a few sessions of mind-numbing, skull-crushing agony?" No contest. Fire up that laser machine.

Here's how the process basically works: tattoos *do* fade over time, as the natural changes in the skin cause the pigment (inserted by the usually pony-tailed artist, who inserted said pigment/dye into your skin with his trusty needle and absorbent cloth to soak up the rivulets of blood created by this mini-samurai attack on your epidermis) to break apart and fade. Laser light simply speeds up this process, breaking down the pigment in the skin. It's a relatively simple procedure if you know how to use the laser machine, and I've been doing it for years. So on with the show!

The procedure goes well, and Food Girl leaves my office in quite good spirits considering she had the second most sensitive spot on her body invaded by laser light to excruciatingly remove a very expensive tattoo.

I wasn't surprised when I received a phone call from Food Girl few days later saying that she was worried because she had a dark scab on both her lips – darker than before the treatment. I inform her that this is perfectly natural. With all that tissue that's being broken up, it's common for patients to develop a scab until the area heals.

She hung up, sounding less than reassured, but placing her trust in me. When she called me ten days later to say that the scab was still there, I began to grow a bit concerned. I asked her to come by the office so I could take a look.

When I examined her lips closely it was clear that this was going to be a Tuesday like no other. What I observed was that the scar was completely gone, and her lips... were *black*. Yes, black! Pitch black. Suddenly I needed a bit of air. I walked out of the treatment room on shaky legs, although Food Girl would never have known it. My motto is something like that old deodorant commercial: "Never let them see you sweat"! But once I was outside the room I began to sweat like a Greco-Roman wrestler. I ran to the office of the doctor I worked for. He was out for the day. Now panic began to set in. What am I going to do? I turned this poor woman's lips from deep red to angel-of-death black. This was by far the worst thing that had ever happened in my career. What could I possibly tell her?

I know what you're thinking: how could this happen? Am I reading the diary of a quack? Well, it's really not as outrageous as it seems. Here's the deal: sometimes when you treat red ink it can oxidize to a permanent black color. The issue in my business has more to do with the laser, and what wavelength setting is necessary for the task at hand. Let me try to paint the picture without blowing out a whole lot of technical jargon. Tattoos, which are basically a drawing in permanent ink imbedded in the surface of the skin, can only be removed by accelerating the natural breakdown of the molecular structure of the ink, which as I mentioned before normally occurs over a span of many years. The laser machine blasts intensified light at the pigments, breaking them apart and allowing the body's waste disposal system to carry them away. The laser we use has various settings; different wavelengths are appropriate for different colors and types of ink. So traditionally, a 532 wavelength is appropriate for red, green and yellow. And

Food Girl was the unlucky winner, as some reds are treated without problem or event. So the wavelength I chose turned her not-so-great red into a hideous black. And yes, I should have warned her this could happen. Hindsight. My only defense – "Why would you pick that dark of a red for a permanent color?" – is no excuse. That's what I get for patting myself on the back earlier this morning.

But kicking myself in the seat of the pants isn't going to help the situation any, so I work up the courage to re-enter the treatment room, where Food Girl seems calm enough. Heck, why shouldn't she be? She's been living with black lips for ten days thinking it's a scab that will fall off any minute. I break the news, which she takes in stride, immediately moving to the "What can we do about it?" mode. I tell her that it's unwise to rush into any decision, and that I should do some research to see what the best options are. Amazingly, she took that suggestion very well, adding that I should work fast. I guess the food show industry doesn't have a lot of work for models with black lips.

After she left, I was a mess. I pored through every book I could find, and was unable to get even a wink of sleep. The next day when the doctor I worked for arrived, I walked into his office, opened my mouth to speak, and burst into tears. He was empathetic and supportive, although I could see him in the back of his head calculating liability. Not a good sign. After much discussion of the issue, his professional advice was a lip roll. Oh my freaking goodness.

A lip roll is a surgical procedure that must be performed by a plastic surgeon. The physician excises (cuts off) the vermillion border of the lip (the outside border that shapes the lip). Then they roll the lips up until a new lip surface is created, stitch the lips and wait for the entire area to heal. It's nearly impossible to duplicate the original contour of the lip, or even the contour of most any normal lip you've ever seen. This is a major surgical procedure for a woman who has merely changed the color of the skin on her lips.

At this moment I think I am going to be sick, so I thank the doctor and excuse myself from his office. Walking toward my office, many thoughts pass through my head: joining the Peace Corps, becoming a nun, moving to the North Pole. My head feels like it may burst from all of the pressure and rapid-fire thoughts. At this moment what can I do? Well, there's only one thing to do. . . call my Mommy.

Is it that mothers are just completely wise when it comes to their daughters, or does the sound of a mother's voice suddenly reawaken the child's brain cells? After assuring me that no nunnery on the planet would accept me, and reminding me that Peace Corps volunteers have zero access to cosmetics, let alone the kind of cosmetic enhancement pampering it takes to keep my boat afloat, my mother asks a simple question: "Have you tried every wavelength available?"

A flash phone call to Food Girl has her in my office in very little time at all. With my laser on the lowest wavelength available, I continuously hit the same small spot on her lower lip. I summon all of my skill and concentration, watching for some positive result. The last thing I want to do is make this impossible situation any worse. Very slowly I begin to notice the targeted area turning lighter and lighter. I have found a solution. Now my hands begin to shake. . . with joy and relief. I inform Food Girl that I will be able to correct the problem, although it would take ten treatments with six weeks between sessions to allow the previous work to heal. Once again she took it all in with grace, and agreed to undergo the treatments. I can only be grateful she had a really cool group of girlfriends who had, for her own sanity's sake, convinced her that it wasn't the end of the world. In fact, they all had agreed to wear black lipstick when in her presence. And they claimed that, for a certain kind of guy, the

"Elvira look" was actually improving their action in the clubs. They also planned a big "Goth" party just to make her feel comfortable with the whole thing.

Unfortunately it would all be fun and games. Because of the intensity of the laser treatments, it would be necessary for her lips to bleed and the scab each time between treatments. And the sessions were not completely painless either. But you can bet I did everything in my power to make the experience as pain-free and pleasant as humanly possible. I gave a really terrific dental block using lidocaine. Lidocaine is an anesthesia very similar to Novocaine, which you've all heard of. I also used ice pack and topical numb cream and a warm blanket to keep her warm during the treatment. Then I spent the better part of my waking hours trying to atone for my sins and earn Food Girl's forgiveness. During the course of our sessions I removed a second tattoo she had added above her left breast (and I ate the $10,000 invoice). I also performed a $4000 leg vein lasering technique, which uses photocoagulation to cause the veins to clot. The clot then dries up and is ready for the white blood cells to carry away, improving the look of the legs.

And, of course, in the end, Food Girl's lips became a natural, luscious, and beautiful shade – you'd never know any of the Goth nightmare had ever occurred.

So, $14,000 in new work, $20,000 of corrective work and continual (deserved) groveling and sucking up was the price I paid to once again be able to sleep through the night.

And I must say. . . it was worth every penny!

 Biography

Having grown up in the relative obscurity of my parents' little farm in Kurtz, Indiana, I might have expected to be overwhelmed by the big city of Muncie. And after also landing a part-time job flying for the airlines on top of a pretty full college schedule, the average person would have felt that was enough to keep them busy for a while. Well, I'm guessing that you've already gotten a few clues that you're not dealing with the average person here. The more my flying introduced me to new places, people, and ideas, the more I longed to stretch out and really make a mark on the world. And my interest in meeting that ideal person of the opposite sex was at an all-time high. Growing up with the tremendous insecurities my hairy arms and chin have given me left me constantly on the lookout for ways to improve my appearance. I couldn't help but notice how the prettier flight attendants received better treatment from passengers, co-workers and pilots. And any time I got a less-than-cordial reception from any of those groups, I assumed it had to do with my looks. I don't know when I first got the idea that I needed a nose job, but by the end of that first summer with the airline, it was about all I could think about. Although I was earning pretty decent money as a flight attendant, I wasn't flying all that often, so I certainly didn't have nose job kind of money. I stopped by a local cosmetic surgeon's office just to be sure my dream nose was really out of my financial reach. It was. But while I was there, I struck up a nice conversation with the receptionist who happened to mention that she was leaving. Next thing I knew, I had taken the job of receptionist. The last thing I needed was another job, but the prospect of being able to add a few dollars to my "nasal hope chest," and the possibility of getting an employee discount made it a lot more attractive.

It was right about this time that I met Jeff, a pilot who would become my steady boyfriend. Jeff flew for the same airline I did, and was also going to medical school. So we already had a lot in common – not to mention he was really cute. So now I found myself commuting between a full schedule of classes, after-school hours at the clinic, weekends flying all over the world, and any other leftover hours at Jeff's apartment in Fort Wayne. Somehow I managed to fit it all in, and I loved every minute of it.

At the clinic, the doctor liked me immediately. Just sitting in the lobby, I would strike up conversation with the patients, remarking from time to time about what enhancement services they could really use. "You really ought to get that mole removed. You're a perfect candidate, and it would totally transform your look." They would make an appointment to have the work I suggested done, and before I knew it, business was really beginning to pick up. The doctor began showing me how to do basic things like laser hair removal. I say basic because, back then, laser was done with a piece of equipment far less sophisticated than today's lasers, which back then , as long as an M.D. was present, you didn't have to be an R.N. to operate. I ate it up. Before long Dr. B was allowing me to assist him in surgeries, and I discovered that I had a natural knack for it. Pretty soon he was allowing me to suture while he did liposuction. Surprisingly, as many things as I have phobias about, the sight of blood and incisions didn't bother me at all. I was always so focused on the result, the improved beauty of the patient, the surgical part of it had no effect on me whatsoever. I absorbed knowledge and technique from Dr. B like a sponge.

And he was more than happy to have me. He was getting twice the work done, with clients asking for twice the services simply because his patients trusted my keen cosmetic eye. I wasn't really trying to drum up business; I would just mention to them the things I'd have done if I had their money.

One day, after a particularly busy schedule, Dr. B called me into his office and dropped the bomb. "As you know, I've been allowing you to perform a number of services that are beyond the scope of your education. I think it's a bad idea to continue that trend." I prepared myself to be fired for the first time in my life. He continued, "I'd like you to go to nursing school. I know you don't make a whole lot of money, so I'd like to pay your way."

I was stunned. What could I say?

"Think of it as an investment for me. The more you can do around here, the more it benefits me. It's just smart business," he explained.

But to me it was far more than that. It was someone believing in me. It was someone seeing past all the superficial things I had always believed were all there was to see in me, and telling me I was of great value. He needed me. And I was more than up to the challenge.

Around this time, Jeff decided it would be a good move to relocate to Indianapolis, and so I went right along with him. Perfect timing. Now that I had added nursing school to my already overflowing schedule, the bigger city of Indianapolis was (excuse the pun) just what the doctor ordered. I leapfrogged into the most hectic schedule of my life, transferring credits at Ball State over to the nursing program at a different school. I studied whenever I could, flew on weekends when the clinic was closed, while still putting in as many hours at Dr. B's clinic as I could. Because I was able to put every skill I learned in my classes to use immediately, my usefulness at the clinic multiplied exponentially. Soon, I was earning more money than the nurses who were training me.

And miraculously, after what seemed like just a brief blur of time, I graduated with a Science Degree as a Registered Nurse.

I felt I owed Dr. B a huge debt of gratitude. I began a whirlwind schedule, giving every available moment to the clinic, hoping that I had found a home.

But by now it must be clear to you that my life's theme song just might be "Don't Fence Me In." As had happened so many times before, the itch to move on began to scream for me to scratch it. The fact that the relationship with Jeff seemed to be on the decline didn't help things either.

Needing a few days to clear my head, I impulsively accepted the invitation of a girlfriend who had just moved to Los Angeles to hang out with her for a few days. Well, not one hour off the plane, the Indiana farm girl meets Mr. Drop-Dead-Gorgeous-Up-And-Coming-Producer. And if that's not enough, he had a limousine. I know, it sounds stupid, but for a girl whose favorite mode of transportation was a moped, well, a limousine and a producer who looks like James Bond just took me over the top. We went out for sushi, which I had only experienced a couple of times before, and I thought I had the key to the city.

Plus, I had this obsessive idea that I wanted to be on the game show *The Price is Right* while I was in L.A.

The next morning after the sushi/limo/hunk night, I woke up at 4;30 a.m. to go to the Farmer's Market, which was next to CBS where they taped the show. No one on this earth wanted to go with me (actually, neither of the two people I knew in all of Los Angeles). So, adventurer that I am, I went by myself on this fool's mission. But hey, they say God protects fools and babies, right? Well, I must have been both. I ended up getting on the show, winning a moped, a set of luggage, and thirty-six Klondike® bars. I was hooked. My life as I knew it would never feel the same. Nor would Muncie, Indianapolis, Jeff, or sadly, Dr. B and his wonderful, generous, life-changing clinic. One month later, I packed up my stuff, sold my moped, and made the trek to Hollywood, aka Botox City.

# Mr. Handsome But Aging Soap Opera Star

He had been a client for quite a while, always friendly and gracious, hugging me at the end of each session as if I were his sister. And I liked him too. I hadn't really seen much of his work, but it felt like he was probably a pretty good actor and fun to work with.

The work he had done was nothing out of the ordinary: the usual Botox and some laser hair removal on his back and whatnot. Nothing serious.

I had really begun to think of Mr. Handsome as a part of the upside. And at the same time I had just begun dating a new guy who I really thought had some potential.

We went out for our second date (I still didn't know him very well at all), and he wanted to take me to a special place – Vibrato, a fancy restaurant with a magnificent hillside view and a fabulous menu. I dressed up extra nice and felt very special as we entered the restaurant. No sooner were we inside the place when my date spotted Mr. Handsome seated at a table for six with some friends.

"Hey, isn't that What's-His-Name from the soap?" Sure enough, it was Mr. Handsome, who my date doesn't know is my client. I have no intention of saying anything at this point, and certainly don't want to make contact with Mr. Handsome, but my date wants to get a closer look.

At that moment, Mr. Handsome recognizes me, and begins signaling me with a frantic slashing motion across his throat as if to say, "Stay away!" It's suddenly clear to me that he doesn't want his friends to know he knows me, in case one of them realizes I am in the Botox and hair removal business. As if! But here he is trying to carry on a nonchalant conversation with his friends while giving me the frantic neck-chop signal.

But seeing this, my date is now wondering just what the heck is going on, and why this soap star is signaling to me like he's my third base coach.

"Do you know this guy?"

I, of course, am reluctant to answer because I make it a rule not to out my clients – a fact that is apparently lost on Mr. Handsome-But-Aging-Soap-Star. As I hesitate, my date naturally gets the wrong idea and figures there's something going on between me and Mr. Handsome. Now he's hot under the collar and ready to walk out of the restaurant, so I give in and whisper to him that Mr. Handsome is a client. He still has a look of incomprehension as I lean in and whisper, "Botox."

Now my date gets it, and can't help but laugh just as the maitre'd escorts us to a table. We pass Mr. Handsome's table and his friends turn and sneak a look at us, but Mr. Handsome, in his best soap opera style, acts as if he doesn't see me at all. The cold shoulder becomes so obvious and uncomfortable that I eventually suggest to my date that we go and eat somewhere else. We fled the restaurant and ended up having burgers across the street.

Two weeks later, Mr. Handsome arrives for his appointment, hugs me like I'm his sister, and never mentions the night at the restaurant. As if it never happened. Strange business.

 An Un-Hollywood Story

Pretty much all of my clients are memorable. Some because of their stunning looks, others due to their inimitable personalities, and another group because of their outright insanity. I don't blame them, though, because most of them are dealing with the pressures of celebrity, the burden of fleeting beauty, or the oppression of money. Sounds funny, doesn't it? To think that the wealthy could be oppressed. I wouldn't know personally, but from what I've seen, having a boatload of money is no walk in the park. Well, it actually *is* a walk in the park (or a cruise on a $5000 bicycle), but it doesn't come without its own healthy share of neurosis and complications. I feel like everybody would come to me if they could afford the treatments. So, it's not the treatments or the desire to have them that makes my customers crazy. No, it's the stuff surrounding their lives that made them insane, but gave them the cash to do something about anything that causes them pain. Unfortunately there are some pains that no amount of money can remedy. I can't help them with those. But a two-inch nose hair. . . I can help.

Still with all of the craziness, there are some moments and some people who are more than memorable – in fact, unforgettable.

The award for most unforgettable would have to go to a woman I'll call Faith, for reasons you'll learn soon enough.

It's mid-afternoon on a mid-week day, and for some reason I'm at home. This is almost newsworthy, because with a schedule like mine there is always someplace to be and something to do. I'm doing something else I never do; watching *Oprah*. The reason of course is purely to do with my schedule. In fact, I hardly ever get the chance to watch television. Hey, I think you've gotta love Oprah. I mean, here's this mega-rich woman using her fifteen seconds of fame to inspire people, especially women, to feel better about themselves while all around her other talk shows are squatting down to the lowest level they can reach to attract an audience. And I confess I'm like most other people. On the rare occasion where I'm in front of the tube and I notice a show where a guy has left his wife and kids to be slave to a dominatrix who makes him wear a diaper while she leads him around the stage on a leash in front of his wife, I have to watch. Maybe out of shock. Maybe for the same reason you can't look away from a gory accident. Or maybe I'm just a sicko. Who knows? And hey, don't worry about the wife of the guy on the leash. She's come on the show to surprise Diaper Boy by telling him she's running away with a dwarf male prostitute. So, as you can guess, she'll live happily ever after.

This specific afternoon I can't help but wonder as I watch a group of women bare their souls for Oprah (needless to say, on another channel someone is probably baring more than that), where do they find these people who are willing to share these intimate details of their lives on national television? Are they for real, or are these actors, hired to simulate these situations that may or may not be true? Even the women on *Oprah*, though it's not the throwing-chairs-and-ripping-off-one-another's-clothes stuff, they're still laying out some pretty intimate details of their lives. Who does this and still can go back to their communities and lead a normal life?

These thoughts are echoing in my head as my cell phone rings.

Now, when my cell rings it's not a simple process. See, I have to be very careful what calls I take if I'm not prepared to go running out the door to rescue some soap opera star who has an extreme closeup coming and a couple of crow's feet threatening to reveal how old she actually is.

To the average person this doesn't seem like a true emergency, but to people in the film and television industry, concealing one's age is a greater art form than many of the on-camera performances. It strikes me at that moment why I'm so fascinated by the people on the daytime talk shows. While I work daily in an industry where each person is trying harder than the next to conceal his or her dark secrets, age, and physical flaws, here are people desperate enough for attention or committed enough to a cause that they are willing to let the whole world munch tuna sandwiches and look into the darkest corners of their lives.

The phone rings again. It's a number I don't recognize, so I have to make a quick decision. Do I take the chance that it might truly be a social call from someone whose number is new to me, but is a person I'd enjoy talking with? Or what if it's one of my obsessed clients using a friend's phone to sneak under the radar and get moved up on my schedule or a quick emergency house call? And don't get me wrong, I love helping these people. I just can't be available twenty-four/seven, and it's easier to not return a message than to tell a weepy Grammy winner that she's not important enough to make you turn off *Oprah*.

In my mind I flip a coin. Heads, I answer; tails, I let it go to voicemail. So what happens when you flip an imaginary coin in your head? Well you end up doing the thing you think is best, and today "best" means being available to the huddled masses yearning to be wrinkle-free. So I answer.

Now here's a great irony. Who is on the phone? One of the producers of a daytime talk show, one somewhere smack in the middle of the taste scale between Oprah and Jerry Springer. In other words, the host seems really interested in doing positive things and spreading spiritually sound messages, but he's not above a paternity test or two to keep his ratings up. The producer informs me that she got my name from a celebrity client and had heard that I could work wonders with tattoo removal and other cosmetic procedures. You have to love producers. They really do know how to say the right things to get people to do their bidding. I feel a bit like a yellowtail bass who has just bitten down on a tasty morsel with the fisherman's hook inside. The producer goes on to tell me that they have a very special person who is the feature of an episode of the show which has recently been taped, and they are wondering if I would consent to donate some of my services to the show for a follow-up episode. All I can think is that they want me to be a part of some outrageous three-ring circus. Maybe the Diaper Boy has decided to go back and be a slave to his wife and her diminutive lover, but she won't take him back until the "Property of Mistress Helga" tattoo is removed from his buttocks. I don't mind rubbernecking this stuff for a few minutes as I'm surfing the channels, but do I really want to get personally and professionally involved in it? But the producer has a kind voice and seems sincere, though she says for confidentiality reasons she can't tell me too much about the person I would be dealing with.

I have to chuckle at that. Confidentiality? On these shows? Gee, I can't help thinking you'd get more confidentiality posting your diary on a billboard in Times Square than going on one of these types of shows. But that's the cynic in me speaking.

The humanitarian in me agrees to meet with people from the show, and then eventually do a consultation with "the mystery talk show guest." I figure I have to do it. The worst-case scenario would be the one I just mentioned. If that's the case. . . well. I'll have a great new story. Best-case scenario, it's Brad Pitt, who needs help improving the un-improvable. Or maybe I might actually get a chance to do something really meaningful. Like I said before, with this show it's a coin flip.

So I go to the meeting, where everyone I meet from the show is thanking me over and over again for coming, so much so that it starts making me a little uneasy. You know, when people start showing you enormous gratitude before you've even done anything, it's like your dentist raving about how courageous you are right before you have a tooth pulled. But they all seem like nice people, not at all the greasy types you'd expect from some of those other shows. After a brief period of chitchat, they cut to the chase and outline for me the story of the episode they recently taped.

Now as I've said before, I tend to be a cynic when it comes to this type of show. But by the time they got finished with the presentation, I not only had tears in my eyes, but a pen in my hand. I was in.

The story: a twenty-eight-year-old woman meets a very handsome but dangerous-looking man. She is excited by his style from the moment they meet. He is instantly smitten with her at first sight, and they begin a whirlwind courtship. He basically sweeps her off her feet, and she is overwhelmed, though she does notice that he has a tendency to become jealous quite easily. But she, of course interprets this behavior as a part of his infatuation with her. After a brief but tempestuous dating period, he pops the question late one night and they race off to be married and live happily ever after. But soon after the marriage his fits of jealousy occur more and more frequently, and erupt into episodes of violence. Scary, the new bride thinks, but nothing she can't handle. The problem is, the husband has as much imagination as he has rage. Soon he begins to weave twisted tales of infidelity in his mind involving his wife and most any male who so much as glances at her. Before long his rage is uncontrollable. That's when the wheels begin to fall off the proverbial wagon.

One night in an envious rage, the husband comes home, his head filled with fantasy images of his wife engaging in various adulterous acts of infidelity. Unable to control his rage, he beats his wife with his fists until she is knocked unconscious. When she finally awakens, he knocks her teeth out with a baseball bat. He ties her up in their home, and then, being an amateur tattoo artist, tattoos his name across her forehead, and pet names he used to call her all over her face. To this day he claims these acts were done to prove his devotion to her, and to make her his for all time.

That afternoon the producers of the show asked me if I would remove the writing permanently etched into this woman's face. Where do I sign?

How do I describe the first time I met Faith? What do you say to a patient who has endured atrocities of this extreme? My gut instinct told me that the less I say, the better. But it wouldn't take long to realize that in a contest of silence, Faith would win hands down every time.

So I knew that I would have to take the lead or these sessions could turn out to be some really morose interactions. I slowly and softly began to outline the procedures we'd be doing, and tried to give her a realistic view of how much discomfort to expect. Even as the words came out of my mouth, I could see the wheels turning in her mind, and a faraway look in her eyes that said, "Honey, who are you telling about discomfort?"

Once again I felt that I was correct in my instinct to keep my big trap shut. In her eyes I could read all I needed to know, and there wasn't really much she needed to hear that hadn't been said before. She had already undergone so much medical procedure, and through the show, recently finished massive dental work. So what could I, who normally use shopping chatter and gossip to distract my patients from any discomfort they might experience during treatment, possibly have to say to her that would be of any real significance?

It was time to get to work. My task was to remove the tattoos left on her grimly-set face. These words that her husband, a man she had declared her love to, had scrawled across her forehead and cheeks as if she were nothing more than a city bus stop bench.

As I began to meticulously approach the crudely drawn scribbling with my laser set at the safest and most effective setting, I could see her eyes grow wide and well up with tears.

Before long, she was so overcome with emotion that her sobs made it impossible for me to continue the work. Completely understanding, I suggested that she take few moments to pull herself together. But a few moments, a few minutes or hours would never be enough for her to get a grip on what had happened to her. And clearly, every pulse of my laser simply brought back horrible snapshots of the nightmarish ordeal she had barely survived. The session was a complete wash.

Trust me, I had no problem with letting her go home for the day. But I so desperately wanted to help her, it broke my heart to send her out of my office without a significant improvement in her situation. That night I found it impossible to sleep. Images of Faith turned over and over in my mind. How could I reach her, earn her trust? What common bond could there possibly be between a Midwestern blonde farm girl who obsesses over the tiniest hair above my upper lip, and this inner-city survivor whose entire countenance had been defaced and violated, making her a walking billboard of violence and shame? Again and again I reviewed the situation, straining to figure out a better way to make a difference in this woman's life. In the wee hours of the morning it came to me, in crystal clarity. That's it! With a wave of gratitude and a rush of excitement I rolled over, eager to get a few hours sleep so I could be fresh enough to put my plan into action.

Faith returned to my office no more at ease than the previous visit. Why should she? Inviting her inside, I spoke as little as possible until the moment I needed to fire up the laser.

"Grab my wrists while I do this work," I instructed. Faith looked at me with vacant uncomprehending eyes. It was no time for explanations, only action.

"Hold my wrists," I repeated. Tentatively she reached up and placed delicate but weakened hands around my wrists. Even at this moment I knew that her hands holding mine might severely inhibit my agility with the laser, but that would have to be the way it is. Time was not a factor in this mission.

Slowly I began the work on the edge of the first letter. Her grip tightened, and her eyes stayed locked on mine. But she did not break, nor did she sob. She squeezed my wrists until I thought I might cry out, but I kept silent continuing my work. And one stroke at a time we began to restore her to the woman she was before.

I understood. When this terrible act had been committed, her hands had been bound. She had endured this humiliation helpless and in pain. It was a situation over which she had no control. She was merely a chalkboard for her husband's rage. How then could she possibly lie back and allow me, a perfect stranger, to etch over the same marks, regardless of whether my intent was to help or not? By allowing her to hold my arms as I worked, she could at least have the feeling that she was in some control of her fate, retaining the right and the ability to stop me at any point. But she never did. She hung on for dear life, and together we removed all traces of her violation.

The procedure took many sessions, but finally on the last treatment months later, I received my reward. Still nearly as silent as she had been at our first meeting, Faith took a long careful look in the mirror. She said nothing, carefully picked up her bag and coat, and heading to the door, turned to me. . . and smiled. Faith was renewed.

I have been a fan of Maury Povich from that day forward.

All In A Day's Work

Monday, 11 a.m.:

Why am I always surprised? Just when I think I've seen everything, my clients prove to me that I ain't seen nothin' yet. I sometimes wonder if it really isn't the circles I travel in that are so strange. Maybe it's me. I mean, in a way, I seem to attract crazy stuff. Seems like even if I worked in a library, strange crap would be going on in there. I'm one of those people who, if I'm walking down a city street, doesn't dare answer that pay phone that's ringing as I pass. No way. 'Cause if I do, I'm sure to get launched into some odyssey that I have no business being in. Anybody else answers it. . . it's just a voicemail that didn't get disconnected. Me? The ghost of Elvis is on the phone with a message for the world.

But hey, Elvis is a lot more fun than a disconnected voicemail. So my life is anything but dull. I just roll with it and hang on to my sense of humor for dear life. This particular morning I need it.

New patients are always interesting. I never know their whole story in advance, so I also have no warning about whether it's a major star, or someone who is needle-phobic, or a nutcase of any variety. This particular morning, I see that I'm scheduled to do a "bikini." That's our abbreviated term for laser hair removal around the pubic area, usually requested so the client can feel comfortable in a bathing suit without worrying about hairs peeking from underneath the bikini bottom, or about a lot of precarious shaving. That's the beauty of LHR: a few relatively easy sessions and you never have to think about shaving again. No more worries about your business being out here for everyone to see. Imagine the boost in self-confidence when you have one less thing to cover up. I love it. Of course, it's always a slightly delicate procedure because I have to somewhat assume the position a gynecologist might. Believe me, it's not near as intrusive as the gyno, but we do get to know each other pretty quickly – up close and personal. It doesn't bother me a bit. I'm feeling like an artist looking over a new canvas. The canvas just happens to be on a sensitive part of your body. No big deal. But I can understand if some new clients are a bit shy on the first visit.

I like to think that one of my strengths is in the way I make people feel at home during sessions. Heck, I'm such a fan and a student of people's looks, and I've been through so many treatments myself, I can almost always find some common ground with each and every person.

So I was a bit surprised to find out that this morning's bikini client is. . . a man. Now, that's not as outrageously unusual as you may think. I've had plenty of male clients who want a clean look down south. Some of them were porn stars, and some just sensitive lovers. In both cases, I'm here to help. So, it's not a huge deal when a nice-looking business-type arrives for the eleven-thirty bikini. He seems nice enough, if somewhat conservative. I've certainly been in this business long enough to have learned that you can never judge a book by its cover. Every individual is exactly that: an individual. Sometimes the ones with wild looks are quiet and contained, while the mousy-looking accountant type is walking on the wild side. So

 Rock Star Pulls a Boner

It's really not a secret that the rich and famous tend to have a particularly low tolerance for rules. It almost becomes a kind of competition between them to see who can bend them the farthest. Like a status thing. As if to say, "I'm so powerful the rules don't apply to me." "Yeah? Well *I'm* so rich, I make my own rules." And so on and so forth. It really can be mildly amusing watching these people order dinner at a restaurant. It would just be too demeaning to order something that's on the menu. So the competition begins to see who can order something that the chef cannot materialize out of thin air. Of course, if by chance the "frog legs with a dollop of rainbow sherbet" cannot be produced, you lose, because this obviously means you don't have the "heat" to make the dish appear. Nutty.

At the establishment in which I work, however, everyone is a star, and it is highly inadvisable to disregard the rules. Our rules, unlike the guidelines the rest of the world follows, were created to allow our clients to leave with the body parts they brought to the clinic intact. Keep in mind, I'm not just some hairstylist who's gonna show you how to wear a scrunchie. This is full-on medicine we're dealing with here, folks. And there are serious guidelines and procedures that must be followed. No exceptions. The truth is, I have made exceptions in the past. And each time I have done so, I have lived to regret it. Let me share one of the most outstanding examples.

I have done numerous treatments over the years for Mr. Probable Hall of Fame Guitar Man. It has always been a pleasure because, his bad boy rocker image aside, he has never been anything but a charming, well-behaved gentleman while visiting our facility. It's always interesting to me when I see clients of mine while they're in public, acting out some outlandish personality traits that are nearly nonexistent behind the closed doors of my treatment room. The wild party-girl diva I saw last night on MTV is demure and bookish beneath that sweatshirt and baseball cap. Mr. Mad Playboy turns out to be a henpecked family man in Dockers and an Izod shirt. I don't know how they pull it off. I mean, it takes all the energy I've got to support the one personality I have, much less trying to sustain extremes like some of these people are lugging around.

So Guitar Man arrives, punctual as usual, but today he has his lady friend in tow. Now, that's not so unusual. I have met and done treatments on this woman, who has the wild hair and large boobs of a rocker chick, but otherwise seems much more like a schoolteacher or perhaps a dog groomer. In truth, her ample bosom has provided several challenges for me as a cosmetic specialist. She has had several sessions for laser hair removal around her chin area, and when she lies supine on the treatment table, I have to push her boobs down and away in order to even reach her face. The fact is, this tends to be the case with many large-busted women, and is honestly just more awkward than unusual. She's usually fairly quiet, and nice enough to talk to. Today's session is a bit unusual because Guitar Man has requested a "partial bikini." Before you get all excited and judgmental, a partial bikini is not all that unusual. It just means the man in question wants some semblance of order in the hair surrounding his pubic area. Often this service is done as a courtesy to the girlfriend, who has grown tired of coughing up hairballs after each intimate encounter. Some guys, like Guitar Man today, just want to get rid of all of the hair once and for all. As I have mentioned before, this kind of service is more commonly requested by porn guys and male models, but I've met lots of regular guys who just don't like the hairy ape look. Guitar Man's lady friend is obviously very much looking forward to the laser hair removal he has requested today, and so has shown up to celebrate the blessed event.

Our rule is, only one patient in the treatment room at one time. There are several good reasons for this rule, and I'm sure you can imagine most of them. But Guitar Man really wants his lady friend to be present in the room while he completes his treatment. I guess he figures he's doing this for her benefit, and probably at her request, so she might as well be a part of the "ceremony of removal." Well, we at the clinic don't quite see it that way, but since he's a long-time customer, and a huge star, it's hard to say no.

So the three of us troop inside the treatment room, the two of them somewhat giddy and excited. Once the treatment begins, I hear a knock at the door, which in itself is unusual, only to find that Guitar Man has ordered food for delivery. As if my workplace is now a picnic grounds. The two of them, of course, see no harm in having a bite to eat while I work, but I firmly announce that the food will have to wait until we finish. They take this news well enough, and begin to whisper playfully to one another. This is just kind of odd because, remember, I'm stationed downtown removing pubic hairs as fast as I can, while they giggle and whisper. Well, obviously the whispering is really good stuff, because before I know it, Guitar Man has become physically aroused. I'm a liberal person, but this is not cool. I rise from my appointed position and inform the two of them that I am stepping outside until they can pull themselves together. They seem somewhat chastened as I leave, and although I am in a semi-state of shock, I hope that I haven't been too harsh. I use the few minutes outside to regain my composure, and am just about to resume the session when I hear what sounds like little screams coming from my room. Now, knowing these two, my imagination can only race with possibilities of what is going on in there. Enough is enough. I charge back inside half-pissed and half-petrified at what I might encounter when I open the door. Inside I see Guitar Man in some state of distress, and his lady friend running around the room half crying/half screaming. It seems they started the picnic once I left the room, tearing into the delivered food while continuing their playful banter, and Guitar Man has apparently inhaled a chunk of food down the wrong pipe, and is seriously choking. It takes me a minute to even figure all of this out, but once I see what is going down I spring into action, lugging Guitar Man up from the table and forcing his naked body into position allowing me to perform the Heimlich maneuver. Fortunately for him, I'm pretty strong, and he's got the traditional rocker physique, thin and rangy. It takes a few tries, but before long I have popped a good-sized chunk of turkey sandwich out of his windpipe. Though it's clear he will live, Guitar Man is still in bad shape from the minute without air. We call the paramedics who arrive almost instantly to take him away on a gurney, with Lady Friend still weeping and shrieking in tow.

Fortunately for her, the ambulance has no one-at-a-time rule, so they whisk the two away, leaving me in shock with a room that smells like burnt hair, vomit and Pad Thai noodles.

The PCOS Kid

I like to call myself the PCOS kid, really as way to remind myself to always be grateful for the freedoms cosmetic enhancement has allowed me, and to remember to keep a sense of humor about the whole thing. PCOS stands for Polycystic Ovarian Syndrome. I have suffered from this syndrome since I was a young girl. I didn't know it at the time, of course. I just thought I was a descendant of the baboon with my hairy arms and pronounced Fu Manchu. Those are just two of the symptoms that include acne (which I had more than my share of), obesity (which I scrupulously avoided), irregular or no periods (which is none of your business), and excessive hair growth (which I have made my business – and therefore yours). PCOS was the source of more than a few tears in my early years, and I wouldn't wish it on anyone. But unfortunately many women suffer from it, growing up with the feeling that they are ugly or unfeminine in some way. I actually discovered laser hair removal before I discovered I had PCOS. Most women aren't as lucky as I was. They never discover either, and live their entire lives trying to cover their "dirty little secret." I still have many challenges due to my PCOS, but no syndrome that sounds like a cowboy's name is any match for Nurse Jamie and her magical lasers and procedures. Still, my gynecologist has heard more than her share of my complaints over the years due to my frustrations over PCOS. There's not a lot she can do for me or this incurable syndrome but listen and empathize. But she does send lots of other PCOS patients so I can do more than lend a willing ear – I get rid of that hair once and for all.

Over the years I have seen a whole lot of bearded ladies like myself, and I've done my best to help each of them as much as possible. But my Little Irene is one of my favorite success stories.

Wednesday, 3 p.m.:

It's been a long and difficult day for the usual reasons. The major cause of difficulty in my profession stems from the same issue: patients who don't follow instructions. I understand why, of course. Most of them are so impatient to see the results of the work they've just paid a small fortune for, that they just can't allow the normal recovery period to run its course before they start trying to force the results. Then, inevitably, they wind up back in my office irate and humiliated because the procedure "didn't work." Of course it didn't work, if you didn't allow even a few days for the treatment to heal. Fortunately, we learned our lesson a long time ago, putting all of the same information I give verbally about recovery procedures in writing in the form of a sort of contract. It's pretty hard for them to argue once they see their big fat John Hancock beneath the same words I've been saying to them. Still, that doesn't stop many of them from bringing major attitude. Some of them, in fact, are in the position they're in simply because they are unaccustomed and often unwilling to take direction from anyone. The curse of the rich and powerful. But ingrown hairs don't recognize wealth or power. They only recognize impatience.

My next appointment is a woman named Irene, referred to me by my gyno for help with hair growth resulting from PCOS.

there's no point making any judgment whatsoever. You just serve each client individually, and try your best to give them exactly what they want without trying to figure out why they want it.

So if this client, whom I call The CEO, wants a bikini and a nipple plump, he's going to have it. Inviting him inside the treatment room, I make the usual small talk, just to take the edge off. We chat about his work and his family, and he seems like a nice guy. But when I ask him to remove all of his clothes, he pauses with a look of discomfort. This usually is my cue to leave the room for a minute so the patient can disrobe in privacy. I do exactly that, stepping out for a moment, ignoring the arched, quizzical eyebrows of the clinic staff.

When I return to the room, The CEO still has not removed a stitch. Gently, I suggest that he can keep his shirt on, if that will make him more comfortable. He does not seem reassured. "Is this really necessary?" he asks. Well, I can't help thinking that it's gonna be pretty tough to get a laser anywhere near the target through a Brooks Brothers suit pants and jacket. I inform him that it just makes the process go faster and allows me to see exactly what I'm dealing with. He stares blankly at me with an incredulous look spreading across his face. But without saying a word, he removes his jacket, trousers, and briefs, taking a seat on the treatment chair. I thank him, asking if he's ever had laser hair removal before.

"No thank you," he replies.

When I assure him that most people find it relatively painless, he becomes a bit impatient and says, "Look, I'll just have the facial I scheduled, and we can talk about other services after."

Would it be wrong to strangle the receptionist who mistakenly wrote "bikini" on his file instead of "facial"? What's the right thing to do? Laugh? Cry? Run screaming from the room? I end up doing the only thing a person in my position can do: I give the CEO his facial, thank him, and inform him that he can put his shorts and his pants back on.

Funny, I never saw him again.

As if I wasn't thrown enough by that, I look at the register and see that the odyssey of the day is only beginning. Next up is The Shriek, the lead singer of a very hot rock band, who comes in regularly for face treatments. It's just perfect. See, The Shriek has a routine from which he never deviates.

His treatment for today is a ten-minute Botox refresh. That means a few tiny injections touching up his forehead and eyes. Simple.

But the routine must be followed.

After a huge bear hug and some grateful remarks about the last sessions, The Shriek enters my treatment room, hangs up his jacket with a hanger we provide. Then he removes his rock-style shirt, rolling it up like a burrito. Next come the (usually leather) pants, which he folds neatly and places beneath his jacket. Carefully removing his socks and placing them inside his rock star shoes, he then removes his bikini briefs, folds them in a perfect triangle and takes his place on my chair.

Now with this music superstar stark naked in the treatment chair, I give him the Botox treatment he requested. You'd think I'd cease to be surprised. You'd think.

cycle that resists the laser's effects, it normally takes at least six visits to really make a difference. Perhaps somewhere in history there was a patient whose hair responded in three visits, but it hardly seems fair to lead a woman whose very heart and soul are wrapped up in this procedure to believe that three visits will ever suffice.

I know what these other places are doing. And I admit, when I was younger I did the same thing. I figured then that my job was to make the customer happy, tell them what they want to hear, and then listen to their complaints later. No more. Now, I tell a patient exactly what I think they can or cannot expect, and if the results exceed expectation, that's gravy. It just works better for everyone this way. And in Irene's case, I want to spare her as much emotional pain as possible.

While my mind is on pain, I share with Irene that the physical pain associated with this procedure is relative. I level with her, telling her that I personally think the procedure is quite painful. But I am a wimp when it comes to any discomfort – and it certainly didn't stop me from doing the procedure on nearly every inch of my body, including a couple of areas far more sensitive than the average chin. Just to put things in perspective, I share with Irene the fact that I could never handle the pain of waxing, but have spent far more hours in laser hair removal than she will ever need. I remind her that many patients opt for numbing cream – about half, actually, provided they qualify having no allergies to the medication. My favorite numbing agent is BLT, which I guess in a way is a kind of sandwich: a mixture of 20% Benzocaine®, 6% Lidocaine®, and 4% Tetracaine®.

Irene tells me she is tough, and will forgo the numbing cream. I guess she would be, having grown up with the challenges PCOS has brought her. We schedule her first treatment, and Irene leaves me feeling better about my profession than I have felt in a while.

She arrives early for her first session, excited, but not nearly as excited as I. This job, I am taking one hundred percent personally. We get to work immediately, and all goes well, though Irene leaves with red and irritated skin, probably wondering why she passed on the BLT. I can't help thinking about her throughout the six-week recovery period between treatments. We schedule six weeks because that is the normal growth cycle, so the next anagen phase has returned by the next visit.

Irene arrives for the second visit, clearly emotionally amped. Even after the first visit she has had to shave only every other day, and her happiness is abundant. Because she now knows what to expect, the second treatment, sans numbing agent, goes much more smoothly. As a patient's anxiety level reduces, the pain goes down as well.

By the third treatment, Irene is already beginning to interview for jobs. She landed a really good one, due in no small part to her newfound self-esteem. By the final visit we had come to expect a whole different woman each time Irene arrived. She was like a blossoming flower, exhibiting the charm and personality she had suppressed for so many years. She joined a gym, and was really working on the rest of her body.

How can I explain how I felt the day Irene arrived for her final treatment with, Nick, her new boyfriend in tow? Irene wanted Nick to meet the people who had changed her life.

And from that moment, she has forever changed mine.

Mr. Yummy, Mr. White-Hot, Mr. Eye Candy

Let me start this chapter by saying that I am not the kind of person who gets star-struck. To be honest, most of the time when a major celebrity is in the room with me I'm usually the last to figure out who the heck it is. I don't know if that's because I just don't care about famous people, or if I'm just always too busy staring at things like dark circles under the eyes, unwanted facial hair, and other blemishes that the average person would hardly notice, to even recognize the star in question. Believe me, walking in my shoes is its own kind of hell. How would you like to be at a fancy restaurant, standing two steps from your favorite movie star, unable to stop staring at a mole behind the celeb's left ear? I can only imagine if I ever got a chance to meet, say, the Pope. I can just see it now. He summons me forward, and of course, I don't know what it is that you're supposed to do when you meet his-holier-than-everybodyness; curtsy, bow, slither on your belly like a reptile? And what do you call him? Your pontifity? Anyway, somehow in this scenario I find a way to step forward as the Great One extends his hand to me, which I take. I open my mouth to speak – and in this exquisite and holy moment I simply cannot resist suggesting that I could wipe out most of those age spots in a single session. Wrong.

So, its very rare that you'll ever see me even raise an eyebrow when in the presence of greatness. Well, that's probably because my eyebrows aren't really going anywhere these days. Hey, not as long as there's Botox in the world. But of course, there are always exceptions. My celebrity exception was Mr. Yummy.

It's not so much that Mr. Yummy is a huge television star. The truth is, with a schedule like mine – on call just about twenty-four/ seven for any screen legend who happens to have been staring in the mirror just long enough to notice or imagine their own personal worst nightmare: a wrinkle or a new hair – well, with that kind of responsibility, you don't find yourself watching a heck of a lot of television. So most of the time my clients' celebrity is pretty much lost on me. But Mr. Yummy is just. . . well, yummy.

I met him through Julie, a long-time client of mine who happens to be a dresser for a lot of big stars, including Mr. Yummy. You know, I have a lot of compassion for my clients. I know their lifestyle is really tough, and in the little time I've spent around them in public, I can see that being famous comes with a whole lot of baggage. People are always watching – in fact staring, judging, obsessing. That probably is fun for a minute, but gets old real quick. But then I think, there's a certain amount of this grief that my actor, singer, model, famous-person clients bring on themselves. I mean, why on earth would you need a dresser? A dresser? Don't get me wrong; I realize there's a need for a wardrobe stylist. Hell, I could use one of those, and I'm wearing scrubs most of the day. You can never overestimate the value of a professional who can tell you what garments make your ever-growing backside look a little less like the bumper of an Oldsmobile. And hey, when you're on the run, or on the set, or even slaving over a hot hypodermic like I am, a shopper to go out and find these items is darned near a necessity. But do we really need help putting the clothes on? I mean, how pitiful would I be if I'm sitting and staring woefully across the room at a rack filled with delicious Armani suits and eight-hundred-dollar jeans because I can't figure out how or muster the strength to put them on? How hard is that? Next thing you know I'll need a chewer for all my meals, and a reader to tell me what the newspaper says, or a wiper to – well, you get the idea.

So is it any wonder the public thinks of these people the way you regard the neon tetras in your office aquarium? Kinda like an odyssey.

So Julie starts telling me about the big names she works for as a dresser, and she happens to mention Mr. Yummy. I say, of course, that he's… yummy; in fact, smoking hot, but he always ruins his look with what I call "the pissed off forehead." You know what I'm talking about: an otherwise gorgeous countenance interrupted by three or four severe lines across the forehead as if you just found out the IRS is waiting in your kitchen to speak to you. Very cute on certain breeds of dog, but not what you want if you're a television heartthrob or even a shoe clerk at Payless.

Julie says, "Its funny you should mention that! He was just talking about taking care of his forehead, and I didn't know what the hell he meant. But now that you bring it up, I know what you're talking about."

We go on to chat about other stars and various other topics of urgent importance.

It's a tricky thing being in my line of work. There is a constant need to put my patients at ease, take their minds off of the work that I'm doing. So it's important to make conversation. Yet, I don't ever want them to feel like I'm interviewing them or digging for dirt to pass on at the first opportunity. My treatment room is like Las Vegas in many ways. First of all, what happens here stays here. Second, it seems we never close. And third, fake stuff – boobs, eyelashes, lips – are considered real. Plus, you can drop a whole lot of cash in a hurry, but look good while you're doing it. Some clients need a lot of talking down, and others, like Julie, it's like flipping a switch: one sentence and they're off and running. All I have to do is nod my head and throw in the occasional "mmm hmmm," and go about my work. And it's kinda strange making chitchat while I laser microscopic hairs around the person's cootchie. But Julie never seems to mind. She goes on and on regardless of what's going on. With some patients it's like pulling teeth. And can you blame them? What conversation would you want to make if a total stranger was doing laser work between your buttocks? Weather? Sports?

Fortunately with Julie it's always easy and usually great fun and lots of laughs.

The next day after Julie's session, my cell phone rings, and who's on the other end of the line? You guessed it. Mr. Yummy.

Now, over the phone, it's kinda weird cause when I answer the phone he says, "Hi, this is…" and then he says his first name – which means nothing to me. You know what I mean? If his name was, say Djimon, I would have an instant connect, but Mr. Yummy has a relatively normal first name. So I'm like, "Yeah?" And he pauses and adds his last name, which at the moment means very little to me because it's now out of context and I only think of this TV star as Mr. Yummy, so I don't connect the name at all. Fortunately, he has the presence of mind to mention Julie's name, and suddenly it's all clear. Now the combination of picturing him on the other end of the line, and the thickness of my skull in figuring out who exactly is calling causes me to become just a bit flustered, so the next part of the conversation is a little bit. . . well, stupid.

Fortunately, it appears that this sort of thing happens to him on a semi-regular basis, although probably less often over the phone, so he handles it all quite charmingly, and before you know it I'm actually communicating beyond the third grade level.

We talk briefly about his forehead, and I reassure him that the procedure is a piece of cake, while letting him know that I'm not one of those practitioners who wants her work to be seen. I tell him that people will simply think he's lost weight or had a relaxing vacation. There's no point walking around with that Nicole Kidman look or "the Joan Rivers" (neither of which is my client, and though I cannot legally say they have had work done, I can say they look like they just came in from a freezing blizzard), when you can have a simple procedure done which simply enhances your already devastating good looks.

We set up an appointment, and that was that. Hanging up the phone, I couldn't help thinking that Mr. Yummy was also pretty much Mr. Charming, which adds quite a few hottie points to his score.

Now, it's important that you understand the kind of place in which I work. First of all there are rules. Because my treatment room is part of a very exclusive, very in-demand spa, there is usually a waiting list to get an appointment, especially for a new client. Old rules, out; Yummy rules, in. He got an appointment for that very same night. That's what happens when you go to a cosmetic specialist who cares less about an Oscar than a great set of dimples.

I felt it was important to prepare the spa staff for Mr. Yummy's arrival. The girls in the office took it all in stride: a few screams and a couple of unprintable remarks. Our receptionist felt very strongly that his name should not be Mr. Yummy, but instead Mr. White-Hot, which didn't go over too well with the clinic assistant who opined that he was obviously more of a Mr. Eye Candy. That's where my years of medical training came in very handy, allowing me to point out that eye candy is pleasing, but not to be touched, while white-hot suggests something that cannot and must not be touched. But, if you'll just take a moment and let the fantasy play itself out in

the proper fashion, what other description can you embrace but.
. . yummy!? Appropriately, the office staff deferred to the supreme
wisdom of my analysis, and dug their heels in to prepare for the
arrival of. . . Mr. Yummy.

There's really no special protocol for the arrival of a
celeb. Pretty much everyone who can afford a treatment at this
establishment views himself or herself as a V.I.P. of some order. Each
person who walks in the door gets the royal treatment.

But not all of them get such a powerful whiff of the latest
pheromone-enhanced perfume wafting out from between fleshy
breasts pushed as high as a Wonderbra can manage. These
preparations are top priority for my staff, though of course, I,
a happily married woman will not stoop to these shenanigans,
although I do let my hair down and apply a fresh coat of "luscious
cherry" lip gloss. I have a professional standard to uphold. Although
I did momentarily consider informing Mr. Yummy that it would be
necessary for him to remove ALL of his clothing for the procedure
(even though the work would only be done on his forehead). And
what, you ask, stopped me from going through with this inspired
stroke of genius? I so badly want to say "professional integrity." But
I have to admit, it was nothing more than the fear that perhaps Mr.
Yummy had undergone a treatment before. How would that look?
Me instructing him to strip down, and him saying, "They didn't ask
me to do that at the other spa."

That scenario is not as unlikely as it may seem. See, in the
cosmetic enhancement world, it's not uncommon to encounter
patients who deny they've had work done in the past, pretending
that each new session is the first they've ever undergone. On a gut
level, I understand why they do it. But when I look at the big picture,
it makes no sense at all. I mean if you come to me for a session, I'm
your dealer. You are jones-ing for it. . . I supply it. Why on earth

would I want you to feel bad about being here, even if you want a second nose planted between your eyebrows? I'm never gonna make you feel bad about wanting to look better. In fact, I encourage it.

The appointment came and went very quickly, as did most of my staff when he arrived. The procedure went smoothly, and he was, as expected, charming. I gave him the usual data, informing him that he would see minimal results the next day, and considerably more in three days, with the full Magilla kicking in at about the ten-day mark. It's not unusual for a patient to be crestfallen at the end of a procedure because they expected to be totally transformed in less that one hour. I sometimes want to remind them that I am not David Copperfield, but simply a medical practitioner who is going to correct an issue that took them their entire lives to create. A week and a half doesn't seem like an unreasonable amount of time to wait for the beauty you've been denied the better part of your existence.

But, I guess it's kinda like spending a day at the car dealership and driving home in the very same Ford Fiesta in which you arrived, even though you left six or seven thousand of your hard-earned dollars in the greasy palm of the sales manager. Who has time to wait?

I also let Mr., Yummy know that I had given him a relatively low dose because it was his first treatment. This is the point where many clients clear their throats and stammer out a confession that they actually may have had a treatment or two that slipped their mind. Now, I have a seriously below-average memory. I sometimes have to check my cell phone to remind myself what my own phone number is. And is it just me, or is there anyone else out there who walks into a room and stands there for five minutes wondering why you walked in there in the first place? With all of that depleted memory, I find it hard to believe that I would ever forget whether I had ever had someone stick a hypodermic needle into my forehead, an inch or so from my brain. There are some things in life that you just remember!

But Mr. Yummy took all of this in stride, and was, again. . . charming.

Three days later, I'm picking up my dry cleaning when my cell phone rings. When I answer, it's none other than Mr. Yummy. This time I know exactly who it is immediately, but I make him say his name so I can repeat it for the benefit of the woman behind the dry cleaning counter. Why shouldn't she have a thrill after dealing with red wine stains all day? Mr. Yummy can't stop singing my praises. He tells me that he's been calling all of his friends, scheduling time for them to get together so they can see how he looks after the "facials" he's been getting. He tells me that his friends can't believe how young he looks, and he feels like every day when he wakes up, he sees a younger person in the mirror. "I am the picture of Dorian Gray in reverse!"

At this moment, I have two thoughts: one, I'm so grateful to have a career that makes people feel better about themselves (even those who have the better part of the free world drooling at the very sight of them). And two, I'm so glad I didn't make this very charming and generous man take off his clothes.

French Swamp Lady

Saturday, noon:

She was actually one of the cutest clients I've ever had, this petite and adorable French pixie with the irresistible accent.

"Allo Jemeeee. . . I yem zo appy to be eyear!" Just precious. It seemed like a treatment that would be a piece of cake. The appointment book had her down for a simple "basic." That's just one of the names we give to laser hair removal around the female pubic region, to make it a little less clinical and perhaps more fun.

There's the "Brazilian," which is described as a thin line of hair on top – the panty line is not done, but in-the-butt is done. Well, if that doesn't scream Brazil, I don't know what does.

Then we have the "Playboy," which is more of a puff of hair on top with the panty line gone, and of course in-the-butt is done. Very popular.

If you want to go a little farther, there's the "Playkini," which I think explains itself. And it goes on and on.

Now, I'm a veteran of bikini laser removal. By now you've probably figured out that I'm not a fan of body hair. So over the years, I've had just about every version of "bikini" you can cook a funny name for, each getting more bald than the last, until finally I just did away with all of it. My gynecologist was always amused with the different styles she'd find at each appointment. It got to the point where she was giving them names of her own. When I had my first treatments I came away with the patchiness that occurs when you've only had one hair growth cycle of treatment. It kind of looks like you've had chemo on your coo coo. So she called it the Captain Stubing Combover. On the next visit, when more hair had been removed, she changed it to the Donald Trump. Then came the Groucho Marx, followed by the Teenaged Boy (which many places actually call the Thumbprint), until I finally ended up where I proudly am today: the Yul Brynner!

But my little French Pastry only wanted the "basic," which is a simple two-inch reduction along the line of an old-fashioned bikini; in my opinion the stuff little old ladies might go for. But sometimes people have to grow into the whole lifestyle of bikini laser. Frenchie explained to me that she had recently had a surgery and wanted to make that area a little nicer to look at. Well, she came to the right place!

Once inside the treatment room, I gave her the customary info about expectations, follow up treatments, and other details. Then I instructed her to remove her underwear while I stepped outside to give her privacy. I left her one of the paper drapes that we provide to retain at least a little bit of modesty before I start zapping hair around the holiest of holies.

I leave the room for a few minutes to give her time to assume the position. When I return, I can clearly see her black panties beneath the sheet.

"Oh, no no, Honey," I tell her, "you have to take off your undies."

She replied in her cute little accent, "I did."

Now I need to look closer, and I see under that drape the most unruly jungle of pubic hair I have ever seen. I'm not kidding. I've been doing bikini laser for a whole lot of years, and I have never seen anything like this. I used to laugh about that scene in the movie *Last Tango in Paris*; this little French number leaves that scene in the dust. It takes me a minute to regain my composure. You have to understand, we're talking about some serious hair here; about seven inches long, with thick fur running all around the crotch and butt area. I have to manually pick up the hair and move it to see what's underneath. I can't help wondering what my gyno would call this swamp. The Lady Godiva? Cher on a bummer?

Now I know why Frenchie has come to me, and in my opinion not a second too soon. I only wonder how I'm going to tame this forest. I don't know if I have a tool that will even make a dent in this underbrush, and I think I might need to rent a machete or a weed whacker! I reassure her that I'm going to give her a whole new look, and she replies, "Oh no, I just want a basic."

I'm beginning to think there's a language barrier here. I mean, she can't be saying she wants a two-inch trim around the edges of this botanical garden. But this is exactly what she is saying. And when I suggest that she might want to trim back the shrubbery before the 'basic." her cute French accent turns snippy as she informs me she knows what she wants. And what she wants is her own pubic version of the fairy tale *Rapunzel*.

So what could I do but get to work giving her the "basic," which in this case makes all the more appropriate the alternate name for this service: the "pseudo."

Of course, the work I do on her is a complete waste of time because no living being would ever be able to see the area I have lasered. So I gently suggest that she might want to purchase a beard trimmer. I'm figuring perhaps money is an issue, and that's why she only wants the bare minimum done by me. I explain that men's beard trimmers can trim down longer hair without pain, still leaving a decent growth. She answers me the way I found many French natives to do: she pretends she no longer speaks English. So that's the end of that conversation. And the end of the session.

And it's the last time I ever saw her. I don't know if I offended her with my fervent desire to mow the lawn of her Bermuda triangle. I swear I was only trying to help.

I keep thinking I'll see her one day in a circus or something – the Amazing Other Bearded Lady! But then, she probably thinks she sees me there as well – the Hardest Head on Earth!

Oh, well.

 The Hiv

Sunday, 11 a.m.:

Seems like a normal day. But in my world, normal is a relative concept. On the whole, though, this has been as rewarding a day as any I've had lately. My first appointment of the day has renewed my faith in cosmetic enhancement. It's easy to lose focus sometimes when you spend your days shining a laser between the butt cheeks of overweight and over-rich women who insist on calling you "Janie" while they gab on the cell phone as if you aren't really even there.

But this morning I did something that matters. I performed laser hair removal on a four-year-old girl, who since birth has had a thick growth of hair on her upper lip, giving her a look that resembles David Niven or Inspector Clouseau. Heck, she's only been in grade school for a year, and already the kids have savaged her so badly she has to be dragged to school kicking and screaming. Her parents have tried waxing, but aside from being really painful for a six-year-old, it just doesn't last.

So it has been my pleasure, in fact my honor, to rid this beautiful child of the facial hair that has defined and tormented her brief time on this planet. Let me tell you, there's nothing like the smile of a child who is discovering perhaps her first genuine moment of joy and acceptance. It was all I could do to keep from breaking down right in front of her. I'm so grateful at this moment for the gift I have been given, butt cheeks later today notwithstanding.

My second appointment of the day, while not as dramatic, has been equally satisfying. It has been my final session with a middle-aged housewife whose husband has been threatening divorce for some time, because he can no longer take the way she purses her lips at him. She can't seem to get him to understand that what he is seeing is merely hard lines around her mouth caused by the sagging of the nasolabial folds that comes naturally with age. And though she may be indeed displeased with her husband, she certainly isn't pursing her lips about it, and most certainly doesn't want him to run off with some eighteen-year-old ski instructor as a result.

Simply stated, as an adult ages, some of us lose the "baby fat" in our cheeks, which gives way to those lines that stretch from the nose down to the corners of the mouth. These lines, however inconvenient, are no match for my Botox and facial shaping. In just a few sessions I have nearly eradicated any traces of the pronounced lines, and my client has informed me that her husband just bought her an expensive piece of jewelry as a thank you to her for not frowning at him any more.

And though I think perhaps it is I who really deserves the bracelet (which she does not offer) I am still so thrilled for her newfound passion that I feel a little giddy.

So when a gaunt-looking male hairdresser enters the office, I am rejuvenated and ready to take on the world.

"Can you help me?" he says. "I got the Hiv."

The "hiv," when he says it, rhymes with "give." Like one word. He says it casually, with no dramatics attached. But I know what he means: he is HIV positive, and has come to me because he wants to do something about the facial atrophy that often accompanies this terrible virus.

And the truth is, he has come to the right place. Among the many services I perform is facial filler. Most of the time I perform this service for people who have lost facial fat, which is normal as we age. But unfortunately, autoimmune disorders attack the fat in the body, a syndrome called lipoatrophy. The face is one of the first places it shows up, because of course, we can't wear a bulky sweater over our faces, although there were years of my life when I seriously considered it. This fat loss leaves HIV patients with that emaciated, sunken cheekbone look that announces to the whole world, "This person is sick!" I mean, it's bad enough having a disease that most people are scared to death of, but you shouldn't have to walk around looking like you just crawled out of a coffin.

And by the way, my man "the Hiv" doesn't really look all that bad. In fact, I think he looks kind of cute and stylish with his fat loss. But you can't go by me. Hey, if I had Kate Moss' or Nicole Richie's body I'd still be thinking about dropping a few pounds; that's how crazy I am. So, if "the Hiv" wants to fill out his face, I am ready, willing and able to do so.

There are several options available to him. The most popular facial fillers include Restylane® and Juvéderm-1 pt. These are good products because they are made from hyaluronic acid, a substance that is already in the human body, unlike predecessor products, which were harvested from cows. But, in this case, I feel strongly that I should go with Sculptra™, which the FDA has specifically approved for HIV patients. This product is classified as Polylactic-D, which might mean very little to the average person, so I'll just tell you that it's one molecule different from sugar. Sweet, huh? The great thing about Sculptra is that it is a thin enough substance that I can sculpt with it more easily. For areas like the lips and the nasolabial folds, those sunken lines that tend to run down each side of your nose, I can work with any good substance. But for filling the cheekbones, I'm gonna need to do some artistry, and I want to be able to sculpt this man's face to perfection.

If all of this sounds heavy to you. . . well, it is. But that's what I do. Of course, every procedure I perform is under the umbrella and the watchful eye of the physician who heads our clinic staff. And as always, I am required to follow standardized policies and procedures, as prescribed by the Medical Board and supervised by OSHA inspectors. As always, I will work on this patient with the same care I would (and probably will someday) work on my own face (once I reach a certain age).

I'm also motivated to do my best work because with each moment, I like this guy's style more and more. Talking with him, you'd never guess he suffers from a virus for which no known cure has been found. He is so positive and passionate, it's hard to feel anything but optimism in his presence. He can't resist dropping names as we prep for his treatment.

"Hon, don't give me that Siegfreid and Roy look, whatever you do. I never thought I'd say it, but go as Renée Zellweger as you can."

He also prattled on about how he also wanted me to do some Botox work on him.

"Girl, these macho brows are leaving lines on my face. You do your thing and I'll love you forever."

I want to earn his eternal love; I think he's that cool. But Botox is not recommended for HIV patients. There are just too many issues with the immune system to start screwing around with injections of you know what, just to smooth out a couple of forehead lines. So I tell him we should concentrate on the cheekbones and play it by ear from there.

Plus, this treatment isn't going to be cheap. I'm hoping he's been doing lots of extensions and hair highlights, because each vial of the Sculptra product costs $1200, and we're going to be doing up to four treatments, four weeks apart. That ain't peanuts.

As it turned out, "the Hiv" needed only two treatments. After the second, in his usual style, he was so happy with the way he looked, he hugged me and said, "Girlfriend, I look like Pierce Brosnan on a good day! I love you!"

As I watched him skip out of the office I couldn't help thinking, "He's got the Hiv. . . as in *live.*"

Teddy Is Forgiven

It's three in the morning. My phone is not ringing; there is no current cosmetic emergency, but I cannot sleep. I sit here alone, reflecting upon my life and the crazy twists and turns it has taken. And when I really think about it, so much of what I have accomplished and who I have become is due to that one fateful day in my life, and that one guy: Teddy Wickman. If Teddy had never made me feel like The Creature from the Black Lagoon, I might never have embarked on this lifelong mission of self-improvement and the improvement of others.

Certainly it's been a kind of obsession, but also certainly I've been able to use this fixation to create a whole lot of good. I can't help thinking back on all of the smiles, the tears, the sighs of relief that have passed through my office as a result of the skills and the knowledge I have gathered and honed over the course of my career. Sure, there have been more than a few moments of insanity, moments of self-indulgence and downright stupidity. But beneath that have been genuine discoveries of self-worth, expressions of gratitude, the conquering of demons and ghosts. I have been fortunate enough to witness transformations of the physical; but more importantly, transformations of the spirit. I have met women and men who were slaves to their own imperfections, and haunted by the reactions and the unspoken thoughts of others. I have literally seen souls set free, simply as a result of the work that I do. And for these shining moments, I owe a nod of thanks to Teddy Wickman.

You see, if Teddy had not been so callous, so thoughtless, pointing out the hair on my arms, I would not have known the pain my clients feel. I might then have thought, as many other people do, that the world of Botox is nothing more than a plasticine, false land of ego and excess. I would never have had the sensitivity to see that the emotional chains of an ill-placed wart or patch of facial hair are all too real. It would never have occurred to me how a back covered with unwanted hair can change a young woman's entire social and sexual being.

I might also never have discovered that there is a key to unlock the gates of insecurity and despair. I'd like to think that because of Teddy, I have personally allowed countless spirits to soar, when all they knew before was being grounded like a wounded bird.

Am I being overdramatic? Perhaps. But show me a little respect. After all, I am the mayor of Botox City. Believe me, I've earned my stripes in battle, and deserve a little indulgence.

No, I am not claiming that Botox and the other tools of my trade are a part of some holy crusade. And yes, they can be abused – overused and unnecessarily administered. There are enough frozen-faced mummies prancing around this town to provide the proof of that. But there is a silver lining in this cloud of epidermis and follicles. And as long as I am in this business there will be a place where people can address their imperfections in safety, confidentiality, and dignity. Again. . . thanks to Teddy.

Years later after our fateful prom date, I saw Teddy Wickman again, just bumped into him on the street. He couldn't stop staring at me. Yeah, by this time not only were my arms hair-free, but a whole lot of other improvements had taken place. Teddy just stood there with his jaw hanging down, uttering the words I had dreamed he might one day say:

"Jamie, you look beautiful. Can I see you later? Can we have dinner?"

What a moment! It was like my life had come full circle. As if I had finally undergone some rite of passage. I looked back at Teddy through new eyes. He was shorter than I remembered; *much* shorter. He was losing his hair, and he was no longer lean, no longer buff, and no longer captain of the track team. And in that moment, I was set free. Free for all time.

Later that night when Teddy knocked on my door. . . I didn't answer. I just didn't need to. I was free.

Many things were left unsaid. Let me say two of them now. Thank you Teddy, for awakening a spirit in me that strives each day to make a difference in the world, no matter how small, fake or insane that world may be. Thank you for single-handedly electing me to the most important position I could ever hold: Mayor of the nuttiest, most maddening, most rewarding city on or off this planet.

Secondly Teddy, all is forgiven. I know that you, and all of the other people in my life who judged me on the outside couldn't really see me on the inside. And now, the inside is on its way to shaping up pretty nicely, so you and all you represent are forgiven. Free for all time. And you will live in my memory, not as I saw you on the street that day, but as the lean, mean, captain of the track team.

And if someday you ever want to make that vision a reality. . . well, you can always come see the Mayor.

Ciao. . .

Printed in the United States
106291LV00001B/96/A